THE ILLUSTRATED BIRD WATCHER'S DICTIONARY

Donald S. Heintzelman

THE
ILLUSTRATED
BIRD WATCHER'S
DICTIONARY

WINCHESTER PRESS
TULSA

OTHER BOOKS BY DONALD S. HEINTZELMAN

The Hawks of New Jersey
A Guide to Northeastern Hawk Watching
Finding Birds in Trinidad and Tobago
Autumn Hawk Flights
A Guide to Eastern Hawk Watching
North American Ducks, Geese & Swans
Hawks and Owls of North America
A Guide to Hawk Watching in North America
A Manual for Bird Watching in the Americas

Library of Congress Cataloging in Publication Data

Heintzelman, Donald S
Illustrated Bird Watcher's Dictionary.

1. Bird watching—Dictionaries.   2. Birds—
Dictionaries.   I.   Title.
QL677.5.H44   598'.07'232   80-23659
ISBN 0-87691-314-1

Published by

Winchester Press, P.O. Box 1260, 1421 South Sheridan

Tulsa, Oklahoma 74101

A Talisman/Winchester Book

Book design by The Etheredges

Printed in the United States of America
1   2   3   4   5   84   83   83   81   80

To my mother,

Florence May Heintzelman

PREFACE

Within recent years bird watching has increased enormously in popularity in the United States, Canada, and elsewhere in the Americas. Many special terms have come into use as part of the vocabulary of amateur bird watchers. This dictionary presents and defines in ordinary language a wide selection of the more common or important terms used frequently by American and Canadian birders. It also contains brief entries for some of the major figures in American ornithology and bird watching. No attempt, however, is made to try to include all possible terms or persons.

The geographic scope of this book is restricted to North, Central, and South America, the West Indies, the Falkland, Galapagos, and Peruvian Islands, and the American sector of the sub-Antarctic and Antarctic.

During the preparation of this book it was necessary to consult various books, including my own *Autumn Hawk Flights, A Guide to Eastern Hawk Watching, A Guide to Hawk Watching in North America, Hawks and Owls of North America, North American Ducks, Geese & Swans,* and *A Manual for Bird Watching in the Americas.* Other books also consulted include the American

Birding Association's *A. B. A. Checklist: Birds of Continental United States and Canada*, Bellrose's *Ducks, Geese & Swans of North America*, Choate's *The Dictionary of American Bird Names*, Devlin and Naismith's *The World of Roger Tory Peterson*, Kortright's *The Ducks, Geese and Swans of North America*, Lincoln, Peterson, and Anastasi's *Migration of Birds*, Thomson's *A New Dictionary of Birds*, Meyer de Schauensee's *A Guide to the Birds of South America*, Murphy's *Oceanic Birds of South America*, Peterson's *A Field Guide to the Birds*, Van Tyne and Berger's *Fundamentals of Ornithology*, and Watson's *Birds of the Antarctic and Sub-Antarctic*.

Several bird-watching and ornithological periodicals also were consulted, especially *American Birds, Auk, Birding*, and *Cassinia*.

Photographs add a great deal of interest and value to this book. I use my own (which are uncredited) whenever possible. Additional photographs were provided by the Smithsonian Institution, the United States Fish and Wildlife Service, Allan D. and Helen Cruickshank, Harry Goldman, Dustin Huntington, Roger Tory Peterson, Eleanor Rice Pettingill (with thanks to Olin Sewall Pettingill, Jr.), Jan Sosik, Fred Tilly, and Peter Vickery.

A few waterfowl flyway maps, and other drawings, were supplied by the United States Fish and Wildlife Service. The map of the American Kestrel nest territories, used originally in an earlier technical paper of mine, is reprinted with the permission of the editor of the *Wilson Bulletin*.

Allentown, Pennsylvania   DONALD S. HEINTZELMAN
29 March 1980

CONTENTS

THE
ILLUSTRATED
BIRD WATCHER'S
DICTIONARY

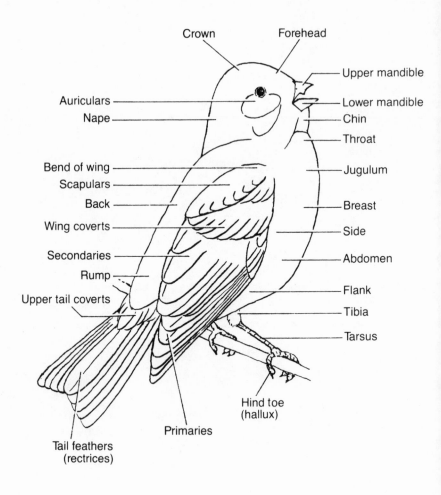

The topography of a perching bird with important regions identified. (Drawing by Rod Arbogast.)

ABA. See **American Birding Association.**

abdomen. The lower part of a bird's belly.

Abert, James William (1820-1897). An early American ornithologist and United States Army officer who collected birds in the Southwest. Abert's Towhee is named in his honor.

accenter. Species in the family Prunellidae. The Siberian Accenter is an example.

accidental. A bird observed far outside of its normal geographic range. Bird watchers eagerly seek accidentals for their life lists.

Accipiter. A genus of hawks represented in North America by the Northern Goshawk, Sharp-shinned Hawk, and Cooper's Hawk. The birds have long, rudderlike tails and short, rounded wings. They live mostly in forests and woodlands, but often appear along coastlines and mountain ridges during migration. Their typical flight pattern consists of several quick wingbeats, a brief period of sailing, then more quick wingbeats. Some North American bird watchers also use the term "accipiter" to refer to the birds in general terms, without reference to any specific species.

Accipitridae. A large family within the order Falconiformes consisting of many diurnal birds of prey including accipiters, kites, buteos (soaring hawks), eagles, and harriers.

The Sharp-shinned Hawk is a member of the genus Accipiter *and is widespread in North America.*

adult. Generally used by bird watchers to refer to birds which have external appearances in fullest plumage development, especially the appearance of breeding plumage. In many instances it is difficult, or impossible, to determine if a bird is an adult by external appearance alone and one simply assumes that it is an adult. Scientists working with birds use a variety of special criteria to determine a bird's age. These include degree of bone development of the skull, plumage patterns, and development of internal organs (especially the sex organs).

aerial obstructions. Physical objects such as tall buildings, lighthouses, and television towers into which migrating birds (especially small birds) can fly at night and kill themselves. Objects with fixed white lights are especially destructive to birds. Thus the lights on tall buildings in most cities now are turned off during the spring and autumn migration seasons in order to prevent needless destruction of birds.

aggression. Behavior which is threatening or actually involved with the physical attack of another bird. Physical aggression is relatively rare among birds. Usually subtle patterns of behavior are used such as threat postures, song, and other actions.

agonistic. Aggressive; argumentative. The term is used by bird behaviorists to denote aggressive behavior between individuals of the same or different species.

Alaudidae. The family containing the larks.

A Waved Albatross on its nest on Hood Island, Galapagos. The species is endemic, as a breeding bird, to this island.

albatross. A very large seabird of the southern oceans well known for its superb soaring ability. There are many species of albatrosses, the largest being the Wandering Albatross and the Royal Albatross. Most albatrosses nest on remote, isolated islands in the southern oceans and around Antarctica. However, some species venture northward across the equator and are occasionally observed off the Atlantic and Pacific coasts of the United States and Canada (particularly during spring and autumn).

albinism. Pigmentation deficiency. In birds, an abnormal lack of pigmentation in feathers resulting in white plumage in birds whose feathers are not normally white. Albinism is known to occur in many families of birds.

Alcedinidae. The kingfisher family.

Alcidae. The auk family.

alimentary system. The digestive tract. In birds the system includes the mouth, crop, esophagus, proventriculus, gizzard, small intestine, pancreas, liver, caeca, large intestine, and anus.

Allen, Arthur A. (1885-1964). A celebrated American ornithologist and professor of ornithology at Cornell University. He was one of the founders of the famous Cornell Laboratory of Ornithology and also a distinguished bird photographer.

Allen, Charles Andrew (1841-1930). An American field ornithologist and collector of birds. Allen's Hummingbird is named for him.

Allen, Robert Porter (1905-1963). A celebrated ornithologist and conservationist with the National Audubon Society. He conducted early hawk-migration studies at Cape May Point, New Jersey, and wrote several classics, including *The Roseate Spoonbill, The Whooping Crane, On the Trail of Vanishing Birds,* and *Birds of the Caribbean.*

Robert Porter Allen in the field in Maine. (Photo by Allan D. Cruickshank.)

altricial. Born requiring nourishment. Refers to those species of birds that are blind, naked, and helpless when hatched from the egg.

alula. See **bastard wing**.

Amadon, Dean (1912-   ). An internationally celebrated ornithologist and Curator of Birds Emeritus at the American Museum of Natural History in New York City. He is an authority on Hawaiian honeycreepers, diurnal birds of prey, curassows and related birds, and avian taxonomy. Among his books are *Eagles, Hawks and Falcons of the World*, *Curassows and Related Birds*, and *Birds Around the World*.

amazon. Refers to parrots of the genus *Amazona*. The Festive Parrot is an example.

American Birding Association. A major North American birdwatching organization whose main purpose is to advance the art and science of looking at wild birds for recreational purposes. The organization's periodical *Birding* contains much valuable information on varied aspects of bird watching, including many articles on bird finding in North America and elsewhere.

American Birds. A journal devoted to bird study, populations, and distribution. Its forerunner was named *Audubon Field Notes*. It is published by the National Audubon Society in cooperation with the United States Fish and Wildlife Service.

American Ornithologists' Union. The leading professional ornithological society in North America. Membership is open to amateur and professional ornithologists, bird watchers, and others interested in serious scientific study of birds. *The Auk* is the official periodical, published quarterly by the organization.

Americas. Refers to North, Central, and South America along with the West Indies and other islands not too far off the coasts of the continents. The Falkland and Galapagos Islands are included. Many bird watchers also include some of the sub-Antarctic and Antarctic islands in the Americas category along with the Antarctic Peninsula.

A male American Anhinga at its nest. (Photo by Allan D. Cruickshank.)
A female American Anhinga.
(Photo by Luther C. Goldman/U.S. Fish and Wildlife Service.)

Anatidae. The family of birds containing the swans, geese, and ducks.

anatomy: Body structure. Refers to the internal body structure of a bird.

Anhimidae. The screamer family.

anhinga. Refers to species in the family Anhingidae. The American Anhinga is an example.

Anhingidae. The anhinga family.

ani. A member of the genus *Crotophaga*. The Smooth-billed Ani is an example.

Anna, Duchess of Rivoli (1806-1896). The beautiful wife of Prince Victor Massena of France. Anna's Hummingbird is named in her honor.

Anseriformes. The order of birds containing the screamers and waterfowl. The latter include swans, geese, and ducks.

Antarctic. The geographic area south of the Antarctic Convergence. Bird watchers include in the term not only the continent of Antarctica, but also the many important islands offshore on which countless seabirds nest. In the American

6

sector such islands as South Georgia, the South Orkneys, the South Shetlands, and the Argentine Islands are included. Some of the world's largest penguin nesting colonies are located on these islands, along with major breeding colonies of albatrosses and other species.

Antarctica. The continent surrounding the South Pole. In the American sector, the Antarctic Peninsula is of interest to bird watchers because of nesting colonies of Adelie Penguins at Hope Bay and elsewhere. Various other seabird nesting colonies also are located on the peninsula.

Antarctic Convergence. The geographic circle in the southern hemisphere where cold Antarctic waters meet warmer sub-Antarctic waters and provide rich marine food for countless seabirds. The exact position of the convergence varies, but it is roughly 50 degrees south latitude in the Atlantic and Indian oceans and between 55 and 62 degrees south latitude in the Pacific Ocean.

antbird. A name applied generally to many members of the family Formicariidae. The Striated Antbird is an example.

antcreeper. A name applied to some members of the family Formicariidae.

antpipit. Refers to members of the family Conopophagidae; also is used as a family name. Several species of flycatchers also are called antpipits.

antpitta. Various long-legged birds in the family Formicariidae. The Black-crowned Antpitta is an example.

antshrike. Refers to several species of antbirds. The Great Antshrike is an example.

ant-tanager. Members of the genus *Habia*. The Red-crowned Ant-Tanager is an example.

antthrush. Refers to various antbirds and certain other neotropical birds. The Barred Antthrush is an example.

antvireo. Applied to members of the genus *Dysithamnus*. The Spot-breasted Antvireo is an example.

antwren. Refers to some species of antbirds. The Streaked Antwren is an example.

A.O.U. See **American Ornithologists' Union**.

Apodidae. The swift family.

Apodiformes. The order containing the swifts and humming-birds.

applied ornithology. A branch of ornithology in which the ways in which man uses birds are studied. Some examples of such use include mining of guano for fertilizer, grouse for hunting, and falcons for falconry. The activities of applied ornithologists also include studies of the impact of birds upon aircraft and how to avoid crashes of birds and aircraft while both are in the air.

aquatic. Relating to water; refers to wetlands and wetland birds.

aracari. Various smaller members of the toucan family. The Ivory-billed Aracari is an example.

Aramidae. The limpkin family.

Arbogast, Rodney Paul (1948-   ). A young American wildlife artist whose paintings have appeared in several books, including *North American Ducks, Geese & Swans* and *A Guide to Hawk Watching in North America*.

Archaeopteryx. The genus into which the first known fossil bird is placed. The species lived about 130 million years ago.

Arctic. The far northern portions of the North American continent and surrounding seas and islands. Generally the area north of the treeline.

Ardeidae. The heron family.

arrangement. Refers to the taxonomic position in which a bird is placed. Thus loons are placed near the beginning of the evolutionary sequence and sparrows near the end (in the American or Wetmore sequence). British ornithologists use an arrangement somewhat different from the Wetmore sequence.

attack. A form of aggression.

attila. Several species of flycatchers. The Citron-bellied Attila is an example.

Audubon, John James (1785-1851). A major American naturalist whose contributions to bird study and bird art include the description and illustration of numerous species of North American birds. His most famous books are the large volumes of *The Birds of America*. The National Audubon Society is named in his honor.

John James Audubon. (Courtesy of the Smithsonian Archives.)

Audubon Field Notes. See *American Birds*.

auk. A name given to several species in the family Alcidae. The Razor-billed Auk is an example. *The Auk* is the journal published by the American Ornithologists' Union.

auklet. A name given to several small species in the family Alcidae. The Crested Auklet is an example.

auriculars. A term sometimes used by bird watchers and ornithologists to refer to the ear coverts of birds.

Aves. The class of animals containing the birds. No other animals are included in this class. All members wear feathers at some time in their lives.

9

avian. Of or relating to birds.

avianphilately. The hobby of collecting stamps featuring portraits of birds. Such stamps may be postage stamps, federal or state duck stamps, or other types of stamps. Avianphilately is a subbranch of topical stamp collecting known as biophilately.

aviary. An enclosure in which wild birds are kept for the purpose of observation of behavior or for breeding.

aviculture. The practice whereby wild birds are kept alive in special enclosures or aviaries for breeding and other recreational purposes. Most bird watchers are not interested in such captive birds except when individuals escape and might be confused with wild birds observed on field trips. Generally birds kept in aviaries wear special leg bands that help to identify such individuals if they escape.

avifauna. The birdlife of a particular geographic area.

avocet. One of the shorebirds in the family Recurvirostridae. The American Avocet is an example.

axillaries. The feathers in the "armpits" of birds. They are important clues to field identification on certain species such as the Black-bellied Plover and Prairie Falcon.

Bachman, John (1790-1874). A Charleston, South Carolina, minister and close friend of John James Audubon. His daughters later married Audubon's sons. Bachman's Warbler and Bachman's Sparrow honor his name.

Badger Bird. A local name for the Marbled Godwit.

Bailey, Florence Merriam (1863-1928). A well-known American ornithologist best known for her *Birds of New Mexico*.

Bailey, Harry Balch (1853-1928). An American ornithologist best known for his *Birds of Virginia*.

Baird, Lucy Hunter (1848-1913). The daughter of Spencer F. Baird. Lucy's Warbler is named in her honor.

Baird, Spencer Fullerton (1823-1887). A major American ornithologist and the first secretary of the Smithsonian Institution.

Baldpate. An outdated name, still used in some field guides, to refer to the American Wigeon.

Baldwin, Samuel Prentiss (1868-1938). An American ornithologist and naturalist who advocated modern bird-banding techniques. He also was an avid conservationist. His *Measurements of Birds*, written with H. C. Oberholser and L. G. Worley, is a classic.

Spencer Fullerton Baird, the first secretary
of the Smithsonian Institution, and a major American ornithologist.
(Courtesy of the Smithsonian Archives.)

bananaquit. A common neotropical species and a member of the family Coerebidae.

bander. See **bird bander**.

banding. See **bird banding**.

barbet. A name applied generally to species in the family Capitonidae. Barbets live in various parts of the world, but the New World species have the most brilliantly colored plumage. The Scarlet-crowned Barbet is an example.

Barbour, Thomas (1884-1946). A well-known American ornithologist, founder of the Barro Colorado Laboratory in the Canal Zone and author of several books, including *The Birds of Cuba*.

barbtail. Several species in the family Furnariidae. The Spotted Barbtail is an example.

barbthroat. Refers to several hummingbirds in the genus *Threnetes*. The Sooty Barbthroat is an example.

bare-eye. Refers to several species of antbirds. The Black-spotted Bare-eye is an example.

Bartram, William (1739-1823). Sometimes considered the grandfather of American ornithology because of his friendship with Alexander Wilson. Thus he also is the grandfather of bird watching in North America.

bastard wing. A part on the forward edge of a bird's wing, corresponding to the thumb on a hand. Also called the alula.

Bastard Yellow-leg. A local name for the Stilt Sandpiper.

Bay Goose. Refers to the Canada Goose.

Beachbird. A local name for the Sanderling.

Beach Plover. A local name for the Sanderling and the Piping Plover.

beak. A term sometimes used by bird watchers instead of "bill." The two terms are interchangeable. See **bill.**

becard. Various species in the family Cotingidae. The Crested Becard is an example.

Beck, Herbert Huebener (1875-1960). A well-known bird conservationist and professor at Franklin and Marshall College.

Beebe, Charles William (1877-1962). An internationally celebrated ornithologist, tropical ecologist, and naturalist long associated with the New York Zoological Society. Virtually all of his articles and books are classics; the monumental four-volume *A Monograph of the Pheasants* is an example.

Beech Goose. Refers to the Emperor Goose.

Bell, John Graham (1812-1889). A taxidermist and friend of John James Audubon. He accompanied Audubon on one of his field expeditions. Bell's Vireo is named in his honor.

bellbird. A general name applied to several species of cotingas.

The White Bellbird is an example. Bellbirds live in the American tropics.

Bellrose, Frank Chapman (1916-   ). An American waterfowl biologist who has contributed extensively to our knowledge of North American waterfowl. He is associated with the Illinois Natural History Survey. His *Ducks, Geese & Swans of North America* is a classic.

belly. The abdomen.

belly band. In a bird's plumage, a broad, obvious pattern extending across the belly. Most Red-tailed Hawks, for example, have conspicuous belly bands.

A migrating Red-tailed Hawk showing its conspicuous belly band.

belt. In a bird's plumage, a broad pattern crossing the breast or belly. See also **belly band.**

Bendire, Charles Emil (1836-1897). An officer in the United States Army, later Curator of Oology at the Smithsonian Institution, and author of *Life Histories of North American Birds.* Bendire's Thrasher is named in his honor.

Bent. Refers to Arthur Cleveland Bent's classic *Life Histories of*

North American Birds, published by the Smithsonian Institution and reprinted by Dover Publications, Inc.

Bent, Arthur Cleveland (1866-1954). The celebrated amateur ornithologist and author of the monumental series *Life Histories of North American Birds*, published by the Smithsonian Institution.

Berger, Andrew John (1915-   ). An American ornithologist, anatomist, and former chairman of the Department of Zoology at the University of Hawaii. He has written many books, mostly on anatomy, but also *Hawaiian Birdlife, Bird Study*, and *Fundamentals of Ornithology*. He is active in bird conservation in the Hawaiian islands.

bevy. A group; especially, a flock of quail.

Bewick, Thomas (1754-1828). An English wood engraver and acquaintance of John James Audubon. Bewick's Wren is named in his honor.

Big Day. A once-each-year field effort extended over a period of 24 hours during which bird watchers attempt to observe as many species of birds as possible. Most Big Day Counts are made at the peak of the spring migration.

Big Day Count. See **Big Day**.

bill. The beak of a bird. It extends forward from the jaws and consists of an upper part, the maxilla, and a lower part, the mandible. Birds exhibit a remarkable variety of bill shapes and styles, each of which is adapted for specific feeding habits.

billing. A pattern of bird behavior during which certain species cross their bills during courtship displays. Billing is used especially by some species of seabirds.

binoculars. An optical instrument used to magnify images of objects such as birds when observed from a distance. Most bird watchers now prefer central-focus binoculars rather than the older models which required each eyepiece to be focused separately.

biology. The scientific study of living animals and plants. Some branches of biology, such as taxonomy, also study preserved specimens of animals or plants.

biomass. An ecological term that refers to the total weight of animals (including birds) and plants living on a particular unit of land.

biome. A major natural community of living organisms, both plant and animal. Examples are grassland and deciduous forest.

biosphere. An ecological term meaning the total parts of the earth capable of supporting life.

biota. The animal and plant life of a particular geographic area. Birds are part of an area's biota.

biotic community. An ecological term meaning all the species of animals and plants that live in a particular type of habitat. In North America the main biotic communities are tundra, coniferous forest, deciduous forest, grassland, southwestern oak woodland, pinyon pine-juniper woodland, chaparral, sagebrush, and scrub desert. Each is named for the dominant plants living there.

bird. A species or individual animal belonging to the class Aves. All birds are distinguished by a covering of feathers at some period in their life. No other animals except birds wear feathers.

birdathon. A money-raising technique used by some Audubon societies to help support their projects. Bird watchers select one day for a bird count and receive an agreed-upon sum of money from cooperators for each species of bird observed by each birder during the day.

bird bander. A person licensed to band (or ring) wild birds for scientific study purposes.

bird banding. A technique used to mark wild birds with numbered aluminum bands or rings which are placed around the leg. The bands are issued in various sizes by the United States Fish and Wildlife Service and the Canadian Wildlife Service. Only qualified persons who receive special evaluations are issued bird-banding permits. The objective of bird banding is eventually to recover as many banded birds as possible in order to study migration routes, ages of birds, and a variety of related aspects of the lives and activities of wild birds.

A Least Tern being banded.
(Photo by Jack F. Dermid/U.S. Fish and Wildlife Service.)

bird distribution. See **geographic distribution**.

birder. A person who watches wild birds for recreational purposes. The term often is used interchangeably with "bird watcher."

bird feeder. A container of various shapes and designs, used to hold sunflower seeds, cracked corn, and other food eaten by wild birds. Birds frequently visit feeders in the yards of homes, and such feeding stations provide an important source of food for birdlife, especially during winter.

bird house. See **nest box**.

birding. The recreational activity of looking at wild birds for enjoyment. *Birding* is the name of the journal published by the American Birding Association.

bird of prey. A more or less general term applied to vultures, kites, hawks, eagles, falcons, ospreys, owls, and related species. Use of the term generally is restricted to birds in the orders Falconiformes and Strigiformes.

bird range. See **range**.

bird topography. The external regions and parts of a bird's body such as crown, breast, and rump.

bird watcher. Generally a person who looks at wild birds for recreational purposes and enjoyment without trying to advance ornithological knowledge. However, some bird watchers extend their activities to include more serious field studies of the life histories, distribution, migration, and other aspects of the lives of birds. The terms "bird watcher" and "birder" often mean the same thing

Bird Watcher's Digest. A popular, nontechnical bird watcher's magazine containing a varied assortment of light reading about birds and bird watching.

bittern. Refers to various species in the family Ardeidae. The American Bittern is an example.

The Rough-legged Hawk is a member of the genus Buteo. *It is one of many species of birds of prey in the Americas (Photo by Harry Goldman.)*

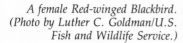

A male Red-winged Blackbird. (Photo by Allan D. Cruickshank.)

A female Red-winged Blackbird. (Photo by Luther C. Goldman/U.S. Fish and Wildlife Service.)

blackbird. A general term used to refer to species in the family Icteridae. The Red-winged Blackbird is an example.

Blackbreast. A local name for the Black-bellied Plover.

Blackbreasted Plover. A local name for the Black-bellied Plover.

Black-head. Refers to the Greater Scaup.

Black-tail. A local name for the Hudsonian Godwit.

black-tyrant. Various flycatchers such as the Riverside Tyrant.

19

blawking. A term invented by members of the Urner Ornithological Club of Newark, New Jersey, to describe the study of migrating hawks from a blimp. The technique was used for the first time on September 21, 1948, in New Jersey and eastern Pennsylvania.

blind. A structure, usually of cloth with supporting poles, used by bird photographers and occasionally ornithologists to hide themselves from view when working close to the nests or feeding areas of wild birds. Most blinds are temporary and are moved from site to site as needed, but some permanent blinds are built near waterholes, bird baths, and feeders. Hunters also use blinds for waterfowl hunting purposes. British bird watchers and photographers use the term "hide" to refer to blinds.

Bluebill. A name usually used by hunters, but not bird watchers or ornithologists, to refer to the Lesser Scaup. Sometimes the name also is used by hunters to refer to other species of diving ducks, including the Greater Scaup, Ringnecked Duck, and Ruddy Duck.

bluebird. Applied generally to members of the genus *Sialia*. The Eastern Bluebird is an example.

An Eastern Bluebird at its nest.

Blue List. An annual list of birds, published in *American Birds*, that show early signs of declining in numbers. If the decline continues such birds might eventually become rare or endangered.

Blue Plover. A local name for the Red Knot.

Blue-wing. A local name for the Blue-winged Teal.

Boatbill. Refers to the Boat-billed Heron native to the American tropics.

Bobolink. A New World member of the family Icteridae.

A Bobwhite. It is one of many species of quail and a popular game bird.

Bobwhite. A small New World quail. It is a popular game bird.

boil. A term used by a few hawk watchers in New England to refer to a group of migrating hawks milling inside a thermal. The more common and widely used term for the phenomenon is "kettle" which hawk watchers are encouraged to use. See **kettle**.

Bombycillidae. The family containing the waxwings.

Bonaparte, Charles Lucien Jules Laurent (1803-1857). A French nobleman and naturalist who lived in the United States from 1822 to 1828 and edited an edition of Alexander Wilson's *American Ornithology*. The Bonaparte's Gull is named in his honor.

Bond, James (1900-   ). A celebrated ornithologist at the Academy of Natural Sciences of Philadelphia and the world's leading authority on the birds of the West Indies. He has written many articles on West Indian birdlife, and is the author of *Birds of the West Indies* and the more technical *Check-List of Birds of the West Indies*.

booby. Refers to species in the family Sulidae. The Blue-footed Booby is an example.

booming ground. The area where Greater Prairie Chickens engage in courtship or social displays.

boreal. Refers to climatic and geographic areas just south of the Arctic.

brace. A pair (regardless of sex) of dead game birds.

Brandt, Johaan Friedrich (1802-1879). A German zoologist who described various mammals and birds collected in the western United States. Brandt's Cormorant is named in his honor.

Brant. A species of North American sea goose.

breast. A bird's chest.

breeding bird census. A count or survey of nesting birds on a given plot of land. Each year *American Birds* devotes one issue of the magazine to breeding bird census results.

breeding grounds. The geographic area in which the members of a species of bird nest.

breeding season. The nesting season for a particular species. Breeding seasons vary widely in different parts of the New World.

Brewer, Thomas Mayo (1814-1880). A publisher and author of *North American Oology*. Brewer's Blackbird is named in his honor.

*A Blue-footed Booby
on Hood Island, Galapagos.*

*A Greater Prairie Chicken on its
booming ground. (Photo by
Luther C. Goldman/U.S. Fish
and Wildlife Service.)*

*Brant (western or black brant
form) at their nest in Alaska.
(Photo by Jerry L. Hout/U.S.
Fish and Wildlife Service.)*

brilliant. Refers to species of hummingbirds in the genus *Heliodoxa*. The Empress Brilliant is an example.

bristlefront. Several species in the family Rhinocyptidae. The Slaty Bristlefront is an example.

bristle-tyrant. Various species of flycatchers. The Variegated Bristle-Tyrant is an example.

Broad-bill. The Greater Scaup.

Broley, Charles L. (?-1959). A famous Canadian bird bander who banded more than 1,000 Bald Eagle nestlings in Florida and discovered for the first time the pattern of seasonal migration for these eagles via an analysis of his banding recovery information. The story of his adventures with eagles is told by M. J. Broley in *Eagle Man*.

brood. The young birds hatched from one set or clutch of eggs.

brooding. Refers to a parent bird's behavior as it sits on young birds in the nest so they remain warm. Occasionally the term also refers to a parent bird sitting on eggs.

Maurice Broun, in 1956, on the North Lookout at Hawk Mountain Sanctuary, Pennsylvania. Broun has been called the "father of hawk watching" in North America.

Broun, Maurice (1906-1979). The celebrated first curator of Hawk Mountain Sanctuary, Pennsylvania. He and his wife, Irma, were responsible for stopping the shooting of migrating hawks at Hawk Mountain and turning the site into a world-famous wildlife sanctuary which is the first sanctuary for birds of prey in the world. His book *Hawks Aloft* is a classic.

Brown Coot. A local name for the Surf Scoter.

brush-finch. Members of the genus *Atlapetes*. The Tepui Brush-Finch is an example.

buccal. Of or relating to the mouth.

Bucconidae. The puffbird family.

Buff-breast. A local name for the Red Knot.

Bufflehead. A small North American duck.

A male Bufflehead.

Bull, John (1914-   ). A well-known ornithologist at the American Museum of Natural History in New York City and authority on the birdlife of that city and New York State. He is the author of *Birds of the New York Area, Birds of New York State,* and *The Audubon Society Field Guide to North American Birds* (eastern region).

Buller, Sir Walter Lawry (1838-1906). A New Zealand lawyer and authority on that country's birds. Buller's Shearwater is named in his honor.

bullfinch. Refers to several West Indian species in the family Fringillidae. The Puerto Rican Bullfinch is an example.

Bullock, William (1775-1840). An English naturalist for whom Bullock's Oriole is named.

Bumblebee Duck. Another name for the Bufflehead.

bunting. Sometimes applied generally to some members of the family Fringillidae. The Painted Bunting is an example.

Burhinidae. The thick-knee family. The Double-striped Thick-knee is an example.

Burleigh, Thomas Dearborn (1895-1973). An American ornithologist and authority on Georgia and Idaho birdlife. His major books are *Georgia Birds* and *Birds of Idaho*.

bush-bird. Refers to certain antbirds.

bush-tanager. Various species of tanagers. The Common Bush-Tanager is an example.

bushtit. A name applied generally to members of the genus *Psaltriparus*.

bush-tyrant. Several flycatchers; the Smoky Bush-Tyrant is an example.

Butcher Bird. A vernacular name sometimes given to shrikes.

Buteo. A genus of soaring hawks of which the Red-tailed Hawk is an example. Bird watchers in North America sometimes use the term in a general way to refer to soaring hawks without reference to a particular species.

Buteoninae. The subfamily containing eagles and other larger members of the family Accipitridae.

Butterball. A colloquial name applied by hunters to Ruddy Ducks and Buffleheads. Bird watchers rarely, if ever, use the term.

buzzard. In North America the term is used occasionally to refer to various species of vultures. However, in Europe the term refers to certain soaring hawks but not to vultures.

Cabot, Samuel (1815-1885). An ornithologist at the Boston Society of Natural History who discovered species of birds new to science. Cabot's Tern is named in his honor.

cacholote. Several species in the family Furnariidae. The Brown Cacholote is an example.

cacique. Refers to various tropical members of the family Icteridae. The Red-rumped Cacique is an example.

Cade, Thomas Joseph (1928-   ). An internationally recognized expert on birds of prey. He is best known for his work in captive breeding of Peregrine Falcons at Cornell University.

Cahow. A name some residents of Bermuda apply to the endangered Bermuda Petrel.

call. A term sometimes used by some bird watchers to refer to a bird's voice, vocalization, or song.

canastero. Various members of the family Furnariidae. The Canyon Canastero is an example.

canopy. The upper levels of vegetation in a forest.

Canvasback. A popular North American diving duck much prized by both hunters and bird watchers.

A pair of Canvasbacks; female on left.
(Photo by Rex Gary Schmidt/U.S. Fish and Wildlife Service.)

cap. The top of a bird's head.

Cape Race. Another name for the Red-throated Loon.

Cape Racer. Another name for the Red-throated Loon.

Capitonidae. The barbet family.

Caprimulgidae. The nightjar family.

Caprimulgiformes. The order containing the Oilbird, potoos, and nightjars.

caracara. Refers to several species in the family Falconidae. Caracaras are rather vulturelike in their behavior despite their evolutionary relationship to falcons. The Crested Caracara is an example.

cardinal. Various species in the family Fringillidae. The Northern Cardinal is an example.

Cariamidae. The cariama family.

carib. Refers to several species of hummingbirds. The Purple-throated Carib is an example.

Carolina Rail. A local name for the Sora.

Cassin, John (1813-1869). An early curator of ornithology at the Academy of Natural Sciences of Philadelphia. He described 193 new species of birds. *Cassinia*, the periodical issued by the Delaware Valley Ornithological Club, is named in his honor.

Cassinia. The periodical published by the Delaware Valley Ornithological Club of Philadelphia. It is one of the oldest and most respected regional ornithology journals published in North America.

casting. See **pellet**.

Catamblyrhynchidae. The Plush-capped Finch family.

Catbird. A popular North American songbird belonging to the family Mimidae. The species also is known as the Gray Catbird.

A Gray Catbird removing a fecal sac from a nestling.

A Northern Cardinal. (Photo by Alan D. Cruickshank.)

Cathartidae. The vultures of the New World. Both vultures and condors belong to the family.

CBC. See **Christmas Bird Count**.

census. A survey of populations. There are various types of bird census, including breeding bird, winter bird, and others.

cere. A fleshy covering at the base of the bill of a bird of prey and certain other birds.

Certhiidae. The creeper family.

chachalaca. Certain species in the family Cracidae. The Plain Chachalaca is an example.

Chapin, James Paul (1889-1964). A distinguished ornithologist at the American Museum of Natural History. He was an authority on African birds and is best known for his monumental *Birds of the Belgian Congo*.

Chapman, Frank Michler (1864-1945). The venerable chairman of the Department of Birds at the American Museum of Natural History. He founded and edited *Bird-Lore* (an early version of *Audubon* magazine) and wrote extensively about birds. His *Handbook of Birds of Eastern North America* is a classic.

Charadriidae. The plover family.

Charadriiformes. The order containing the shorebirds, gulls, terns, and auks.

chat. Refers to several species of wood warblers. The Yellow-breasted Chat is an example.

chat-tyrant. Several species of flycatchers. The Crowned Chat-Tyrant is an example.

chest. The breast.

chick. A very young bird still in the nest or, in some cases, just out of the nest.

chickadee. Several songbirds in the genus *Parus*. The Black-capped Chickadee is an example.

A Black-capped Chickadee. (Photo by Harry Goldman.)

Christmas Bird Count. Annual one-day Christmas season field trips, restricted to a circle 15 miles in diameter, during which bird watchers attempt to count as many species and individuals of birds as possible within the assigned circle. Within recent years more than 1,000 such Christmas Bird Counts have been conducted in North America by bird watchers. The counts are coordinated by the National Audubon Society and the results published once every year in *American Birds*.

Christmas Card Bird Count. A count of the number of species of birds shown on the Christmas cards one receives during the Christmas season.

Christmas Count. See **Christmas Bird Count**.

Ciconiidae. The stork family.

Ciconiiformes. The order containing the herons, Boat-billed Heron, storks, ibises, and flamingos.

Cinclidae. The dipper family.

Cinclodes. Various species in the family Furnariidae. The Blackish Cinclodes is an example.

Clam-bird. A local name for the Piping Plover.

Clark, William (1770-1838). A captain in the United States Army and one of the leaders of the famous Lewis and Clark expedition. Clark's Nutcracker is named in his honor.

class. A higher taxonomic category containing a major group of animals (such as birds). Birds belong to the class Aves.

clutch. A complete set of eggs laid by one female bird in her nest. Clutch size varies from species to species, and from individual to individual within a species. However, each species has a maximum number of eggs laid per clutch.

cob. A male swan.

Cochleariidae. The Boat-billed Heron family.

cock. A male bird, especially a game bird.

cock-of-the-rock. Refers to two South American species in the genus *Rupicola*. The Andean Cock-of-the-Rock is an example.

Cock-of-the-Woods. A vernacular name sometimes used in Trinidad for the Black-faced Antthrush.

collar. A band of distinctively colored feathers circling the neck of a bird.

colony. A group of birds nesting in close proximity to one another. Many herons, egrets, gulls, terns, and seabirds nest in colonies.

Columbidae. The pigeon and dove family.

Columbiformes. The order containing the pigeons, doves, and sandgrouse.

An adult California Condor in flight.
(Photo by Fred Sibley/U.S. Fish and Wildlife Service.)

comet. Refers to several species of hummingbirds. The Red-tailed Comet is an example.

condor. A name applied either to the Andean or the California Condor. A very large vulture in the family Cathartidae.

conebill. Various species in the family Coerebidae. The Bicolored Conebill is an example.

Connolly, Jerome Patrick (1931-   ). A widely known American wildlife artist perhaps best known for his splendid diorama backgrounds in many leading natural history museums. His paintings also appear in leading conservation magazines and numerous books.

Conopophagidae. The antpipit family.

Conover, Boardman (1892-1950). An ornithologist and sportsman with a particular interest in game birds. He is best known for the completion of the last four volumes of the *Catalogue of the Birds of the Americas.*

Coop. A term used by many hawk watchers to refer to a Cooper's Hawk. The term is used commonly at many eastern hawk migration lookouts.

Cooper, William C. (1798-1864). An early New York naturalist. The Cooper's Hawk is named in his honor.

coot. Various species in the family Rallidae. The American Coot is an example.

American Coots at a national wildlife refuge.

33

A pair of Mallards copulating.

copulation. The sexual union of a male with a female whereby the male transfers sperm into the female for the fertilization of eggs. The act of mating.

coquette. Refers to hummingbirds in the genus *Lophornis*. The Tufted Coquette is an example. Coquettes are unusually ornate hummingbirds and are among the most attractive members of the family.

Coraciiformes. The order containing the kingfishers, todies, motmots, and certain other families.

cormorant. Refers to species in the family Phalacorcoracidae. The Double-crested Cormorant is an example.

A flock of Double-crested Cormorants in flight.

coronet. Hummingbirds in the genus *Boissonneaua*. The Velvet-purple Coronet is an example.

Corvidae. The family containing ravens, crows, and jays.

Cory, Charles Barney (1857-1921). An ornithologist connected with the Field Museum in Chicago. Cory's Shearwater is named in his honor.

cosmopolitan. A term applied to birds which are distributed more or less throughout the world. The Barn Owl is an example of a species with a cosmopolitan distribution.

cost per bird. The amount of money required to see a given species of bird in respect to travel, lodging, and food costs. Generally birds visiting backyard bird feeders cost almost nothing to see whereas the cost per bird for species such as wild penguins in Antarctica is very substantial.

cotinga. Refers to various tropical species, some vividly colored, of the family Cotingidae. The Spangled Cotinga is an example.

Cotingidae. The tropical family containing cotingas, bellbirds, fruit-crows, and similar species.

Coues, Elliott (1842-1899). One of the most distinguished and important of American ornithologists in the last century. He is best known for his monumental *Key to North American Birds*.

Elliott Coues, one of the most important American ornithologists of the last century. (Photo courtesy of the Smithsonian Archives.)

cover. Refers to the vegetation in an area in which birds seek refuge, safety, food, and nesting sites.

covert. Small feathers covering the bases of the flight feathers on a bird's wings and tail. Feathers covering the ears also are called ear coverts. Occasionally the term is used to refer to habitat in which birds find concealment or shelter.

covey. Refers to a small flock of grouse or partridge. See also **pack**.

cowbird. Refers to various species in the family Icteridae. The Brown-headed Cowbird is an example.

CPB. See **cost per bird**.

Cracidae. The family containing chachalacas, guans, and curassows.

crake. Various species in the family Rallidae. The Dot-winged Crake is an example.

crane. Refers to species in the family Gruidae. The Whooping Crane is an example.

Craveri, Frederico (1815-1890). An Italian zoologist and scientist who collected birds on islands off Lower California. The Craveri's Murrelet is named in his honor.

creche. A group or collection of young penguins of one or several species which are attended to by a few adults.

Creek Broad-bill. The Lesser Scaup.

Creek Duck. An obscure name for the Gadwall.

creeper. Species in the genus *Certhia*. The Brown Creeper is an example.

crescentchest. Several species in the family Rhinocryptidae. The Elegant Crescentchest is an example.

crissum. Term used by some bird watchers, especially hawk watchers, to refer to a bird's undertail coverts.

crop. A saclike extension of the esophagus used to store food. In some birds, especially hawks, a full crop is readily visible.

crossbill. Peculiar species in the genus *Loxia*. The Red Cross-bill is an example. The unusual crossed bill is used to extract seeds from pine cones.

cross fostering. A technique used by raptor managers whereby very young birds of prey hatched in captivity are placed in the nest of another species of raptor to be reared. The Pere-grine Falcon chicks may be placed in a Prairie Falcon's nest to be reared by the host species. The technique is experimental and subject to continued critical evaluation.

An American Crow.

crow. Species in the genus *Corvus* of the family Corvidae. The American Crow is an example.

crown. The top of a bird's head.

Cruickshank, Allan D. (1907-1974). A celebrated American orni-thologist, bird photographer, and conservationist employed by the National Audubon Society. He was one of the foun-ders of the Bronx County Bird Club and taught bird study for several decades at the Audubon Camp of Maine. He also was one of the most popular Audubon Wildlife Film lecturers; his superb film lectures reached more than a mil-

Allan D. Cruickshank, with his favorite Graflex camera, on the
Bear River Migratory Bird Refuge, Utah.
He was one of the world's most celebrated bird photographers.
(Photo by Helen G. Cruickshank.)

A Long-billed Curlew.
(Photo by Luther C.
Goldman/U.S. Fish and
Wildlife Service.)

lion people in most states. The famous bird sanctuary on
Eastern Egg Rock off the coast of Maine now is named the
Allan D. Cruickshank Wildlife Sanctuary in his honor.

Cruickshank, Helen Gere (1907-   ). A well-known American bird photographer, author of bird books, and conservationist. She is the wife of Allan D. Cruickshank. Her photographs have appeared in numerous publications, and her many books include *Bird Islands Down East*, *Flight into Sunshine*, and *A Paradise of Birds.*.

cuckoo. Species in the family Cuculidae. The Black-billed Cuckoo is an example.

Cuculidae. The cuckoo family.

Cuculiformes. The order containing the cuckoos.

curassow. Refers to various species in the family Cracidae. The Helmeted Curassow is an example.

curlew. Various shorebirds in the genus *Numenius*. The Long-billed Curlew is an example.

Cyclarhidae. The pepper-shrike family.

cygnet. A young swan.

Dabchick. Another name for the Pied-billed Grebe.

dacnis. Refers to various honeycreepers in the genus *Dacnis*. The Blue Dacnis is an example.

dancing ground. An area used by Sharp-tailed Grouse to engage in social displays.

Dapper. The Bufflehead.

Darter. Used by some bird watchers to refer to the American Anhinga. The name Blue Darter also can refer to the Cooper's Hawk, whereas Little Blue Darter sometimes is used to refer to the Sharp-shinned Hawk.

Darwin's Finch. A general term used to refer to finches of the subfamily Geospizinae which are endemic to the Galapagos Islands (and an additional species on the Cocos Islands). The birds also are referred to as Galapagos Finches. They played important roles in helping Charles Darwin arrive at his theory of evolution.

decoy. A replica of a given bird, set in an appropriate habitat, to attract birds close to the decoy. Geese and duck decoys are widely used by hunters. Shorebird decoys also were used regularly earlier in this century to market hunters. Artificial Great Horned Owl decoys often are used as lures on hawk lookouts to attract migrating hawks closer to the lookouts for better observation or photography purposes.

An artificial Great Horned Owl decoy such as those sometimes used by hawk watchers at eastern hawk migration lookouts.

Deignan, Herbert Girton (1906-1968). A Smithsonian Institution ornithologist and authority on the birds of southeast Asia. He is best known for his *Checklist of the Birds of Thailand*. He was a student at Princeton University of Charles H. Rogers.

Delaware Valley Ornithological Club. One of the oldest and most respected regional ornithological organizations in the

United States. The club was founded in 1890 and maintains its meeting place at the Academy of Natural Sciences of Philadelphia. Many of the academy's professional ornithologists have played key roles in the affairs of the club over the years. Perhaps the most significant role was played by Witmer Stone. The club publishes a journal, *Cassinia*, which contains articles and notes of ornithological interest for eastern Pennsylvania, southern New Jersey, and Delaware. In recent years the emphasis of many DVOC members has been less on regional ornithology and more on regional bird watching. Among the major books published by the club are Witmer Stone's *Bird Studies at Old Cape May* and Earl Poole's *Pennsylvania Birds*.

Dendrocolaptidae. The woodcreeper family.

dichromatic. Having two colors or color phases. Refers to two color phases of the plumage of a species. An example is the Screech Owl, which is found in red and gray color phases. However, not all species of birds are dichromatic. The phenomenon is sex-linked in some species, but not in others.

Didapper. A local name for the Pied-billed Grebe.

dimorphism. See **sexual dimorphism**.

Diomedeidae. The family containing the albatrosses. The Black-browed Albatross is an example.

dipper. Refers to species in the family Cinclidae. The White-capped Dipper is an example.

Dipper Duck. Refers to the Bufflehead.

display. Refers to certain special types of bird behavior, either visual or auditory, that serve as the language of a particular species. The purpose of displays is to serve as social signals of one type or another. Courtship displays are examples.

distribution. See **geographic distribution**.

diver. A British term used to refer to loons. It is not used widely by North American bird watchers.

diversion line. A topographic feature, usually long, which induces migrating birds to alter their direction of flight and diverts them toward a new direction. The new direction of flight then is followed for varying distances. The term "leading line" means the same thing. Many species of migrating hawks are especially prone to following diversion lines in North America, but many other nonraptorial birds also use them.

diving ducks. Refers to members of the waterfowl subfamily Aythyinae. Some examples are Redheads, Canvasbacks, Ring-necked Ducks, scaups, goldeneyes, and other species.

A male Ring-necked Duck, one of various species
of North American diving ducks. (Photo by Jan Sosik.)

diving petrel. Species in the family Pelecanoididae. The Peruvian Diving Petrel is an example.

dog-leg migration. A bird migration route with a large twist or bend in the route. Whistling Swans follow a dog-leg migration route.

Dopper. The Bufflehead.

doradito. Several species of flycatchers. The Crested Doradito is an example.

dotterel. Several species of shorebirds in the family Charadriidae. The Rufous-chested Dotterel is an example.

double clutching. A technique used by raptor managers whereby the first set of eggs deposited by a hawk or other raptor is removed (and perhaps placed in laboratory incubators or the nest of the same species in another part of the species' geographic range) and the bird is induced to lay another clutch. The technique was developed to offset the negative impact of DDT upon raptor reproduction in some sections of North America.

dove. Various species in the family Columbidae. The Mourning Dove is an example.

A Mourning Dove. (Photo by Allen M. Pearson/U.S. Fish and Wildlife Service.)

dowitcher. Two species of shorebirds in the genus *Limnodromus*. The Short-billed Dowitcher is an example.

down. The soft body feathers of waterfowl and other birds. Many nestling birds are covered with a natal down, or a second down at a slightly older age.

drake. A male duck.

duck. Various species of waterfowl, usually of the surface-feeding types. The American Black Duck is an example.

duckling. A young duck.

Dulidae. The palmchat family.

duck stamp. A federal stamp, issued annually by the United States Department of the Interior. The money from the sales of duck stamps is used to help support federal waterfowl conservation programs. Included is the purchase of national wildlife refuge lands. All waterfowl hunters are required to buy a federal duck stamp before they engage in waterfowl hunting. The law providing for the sale of duck stamps was approved in 1934.

Ducks Unlimited. A major waterfowl conservation organization whose members mostly are sportsmen. The organization has branches in Canada, the United States, and Mexico. Ducks Unlimited spends large sums of money to protect and manage waterfowl breeding areas in Canada and elsewhere and is a major force in conserving North American waterfowl.

dummy nest. A nest built by a male wren as part of his courtship behavior, but not used by the female. The female wren builds her own nest in which to deposit eggs and raise her own. Male marsh wrens are especially noted for their construction of dummy nest.

DVOC. See **Delaware Valley Ornithological Club**.

Dwight, Jonathan (1858-1929). A physician and celebrated American ornithologist at the American Museum of Natural History. He is best known for his book *Sequence of Plumage and Moults of the Passerine Birds of New York*.

eagle. A large diurnal bird of prey. Golden Eagles and Bald Eagles are typical North American examples. The latter is the national bird of the United States of America.

earthcreeper. Various species in the family Furnariidae. The Rock Earthcreeper is an example.

echo flight. Refers to large migratory movements of certain birds (such as Northern Goshawks), at irregular intervals, following soon after a major eruption or invasion of the species. Thus a major southward invasion of Northern Goshawks occurred in 1972 in the United States, and a smaller but notable echo flight was noted in 1973.

Eckelberry, Donald Richard (1921-   ). An internationally known bird and wildlife artist best known for his book illustrations, including those in *A Guide to the Birds of Trinidad and Tobago*.

eclipse plumage. A curious feature of male ducks in the northern hemisphere. The birds wear the so-called eclipse plumage for about two months beginning when the female starts

Bald Eagles feeding on a deer carcass in winter.
(Photo by John E. Swedberg.)

incubation of her eggs in the nest, and continuing during the summer. The males become shy, form flocks, and lose their flight feathers, thus rendering them flightless for the duration of the molt. Many birds in eclipse plumage wear dull-brown dress similar to that of females. In autumn, the eclipse plumage is molted and the males gradually develop their full breeding plumage. Some southern-hemisphere waterfowl also wear eclipse plumage.

ecology. The scientific study of the interrelationships of plants and animals to each other and their environments.

ecosystem. A more or less well-defined natural area in which living and nonliving components are included. A river is an example.

egg. The ovum. A bird's egg is protected within a hard shell before being deposited by a female in her nest. There are many sizes, shapes, and colors of bird eggs.

A Great Egret at its nest. (Photo by Allan D. Cruickshank.)

A male Common Eider.

egg tooth. A small hard calcium structure on the top of a young bird's bill. It is used by the bird to free itself from the inside of the egg. The egg tooth eventually disappears after hatching.

egret. Refers to various species in the family Ardeidae. The Great Egret is an example. Most (but not all) egrets are white.

eider. Refers to various sea ducks. The Common Eider is an example.

elaenia. Various difficult-to-identify flycatchers. The Large Elaenia is an example.

emerald. Refers to various species of hummingbirds. The Puerto Rican Emerald is an example.

endangered species. A species of bird, or other form of wildlife or plant life, whose entire population is so reduced in numbers as to cause grave concern for the survival of the species. It is likely that some endangered species will become extinct. The Whooping Crane is an example.

Endangered Species Technical Bulletin. A monthly bulletin, issued by the United States Fish and Wildlife Service, in which the latest information on endangered species and their management programs are discussed. It is a rich source of information on the current status of endangered species in the United States and elsewhere.

The Whooping Crane is one of the endangered species of birds in the United States and Canada. (Photo by W. F. Kubichek/U.S. Fish and Wildlife Service.)

endemic. Native to or restricted to a region. Refers to a species or other taxonomic category that is confined to a specific geographic area such as an island but does not naturally occur elsewhere. The Puertan Rican Parrot, for example, is endemic to Puerto Rico.

Errington, Paul Lester (1902-1962). An internationally celebrated wildlife ecologist and an expert on predation. He wrote classic studies on Bobwhites, Great Horned Owls, and especially muskrats.

ethology. The scientific study of the behavior of wild animals, usually in their natural habitats but sometimes in captivity. Among birds the behavior of waterfowl is especially well known.

euphonia. Various types of tanagers. The Orange-billed Euphonia is an example.

Eurypygidae. The Sunbittern family.

exotic. Used by bird watchers to refer to a species which is not native to a particular country or continent and which has not been successfully introduced and established in the country or continent in which it is observed.

extinct. Said of a species or subspecies which has died out naturally or been exterminated due to some actions of man. The Labrador Duck is an example. The extinction of species of birds and other wildlife is continuing, particularly in tropical parts of the world where destruction of unique tropical forest habitats were essential to the survival of numerous rare species.

eyas. A term used by falconers to refer to nestling hawks or falcons. Bird watchers use the term occasionally.

eyrie. A falconer's term which refers to the nest of an eagle or other large diurnal bird of prey.

fairy. Refers to hummingbirds in the genus *Heliothryx.* The Black-eared Fairy is an example.

Falco. The genus of falcons within the family Falconidae. The Peregrine Falcon is an example.

falcon. A long-winged, long-tailed raptor classified in the genus *Falco.* The Gyrfalcon is an example.

falconet. Refers to several small species of falconlike birds. The Spot-winged Falconet is an example.

Falconidae. A family within the order Falconiformes. It contains the true falcons, caracaras, and other related species of diurnal birds of prey.

Falconiforms. The order containing the diurnal birds of prey, including vultures, kites, hawks, eagles, harriers, the Osprey, caracaras, falcons, and related species.

falconiformologist. A term used occasionally by bird watchers, especially hawk watchers, to refer to persons with interests limited mostly to diurnal birds of prey and especially to hawk migrations.

The Peregrine Falcon is one member of the genus Falco.

falconry. The ancient art of training a wild falcon or other bird of prey to hunt game animals, then return to the trainer, who is known as a falconer.

family. A higher taxonomic category containing one or more genera all of which more or less exhibit some evolutionary relationships to each other. The family Parulidae, containing the wood warblers, is an example. One or more families form an order of birds.

fauna. The animal life native to a particular geographic area.

feather. An external structure which, when combined with other feathers, forms the plumage or outside covering of a bird's body. There are many types of feathers, each located on different areas of a bird. No other animals except birds wear feathers.

feral. Wild or having escaped from domestication and become wild. Generally refers to individuals or populations of introduced or domesticated birds which have established themselves as breeding birds in the world. The Mute Swan is an example in some sections of the eastern United States.

Field Bird. A local name for the American Golden Plover.

field guide. A small pocket-size book which provides brief written descriptions of the species of an area along with illustrations of the birds. Roger Tory Patterson's *A Field Guide to the Birds* is an example. Special field guides for specific types of bird watching now are beginning to be published. The author's *A Guide to Hawk Watching in North America* is an example. It contains species descriptions and illustrations along with directions for visiting numerous hawk and eagle watching sites. W. B. Alexander's *Birds of the Ocean* is another example of a special field guide dealing with seabirds.

field mark. Refers to characteristics such as colors, markings, shapes, and/or behavior patterns that help bird watchers recognize and identify one species of bird from all others. Field marks are more obvious, and thus helpful, in some species of birds than in others.

finch. A general term used to refer to various species in the family Fringillidae. The Purple Finch is an example.

finch year. A bird watcher's term used to refer to a winter in which unusually large numbers of northern species of finches, grosbeaks, crossbills, and other Frigillidae appear south of their normal winter ranges.

The Mute Swan was introduced into North America from Europe. Now it is feral (wild) in a few locations in North America.

finfoot. An alternative name for a sungrebe.

Fisher, Albert Kenrick (1856-1948). A major economic ornithologist and one of the co-founders of the former Division of Economic Ornithology and Mammalogy in the United States Department of Agriculture. His *The Hawks and Owls of the United States and Their Relation to Agriculture* is a classic and helped to pave the way for raptor protection laws in many states and eventually nationally.

Fish Hawk. A name sometimes applied to the Osprey.

fishing. Used to describe the hunting and/or fishing behavior of some birds such as egrets, cormorants, the Osprey, etc. The term applies to those species that capture and eat fish.

flamingo. Refers to species in the family Phoenicopteridae. The American Flamingo is an example.

flatbill. Various flycatchers in the family Tyrannidae. The Eye-ringed Flatbill is an example.

fledged. Refers to the period in the life of a young bird when it acquires its first set of true feathers (other than down).

fledgling. A young bird just after it has left the nest but may still be dependent upon its parents for food.

Fleming, James Henry (1872-1940). A well-known Canadian ornithologist who wrote extensively about Canada's birdlife.

flicker. A general name sometimes applied to woodpeckers in the genus *Colaptes*. Flickers are relatively primitive members of the woodpecker family. The Common Flicker is an example.

flight. The aerial method of locomotion used by most species of birds. There are many types of flight, including flapping, gliding, soaring, and hovering.

flight line. A term used by many hawk watchers, and sometimes by other ornithologists and bird watchers, to refer to a local or regional migration route used by birds regularly. Thus hawk watchers often refer to a flight line of hawks along a particular topographic feature.

flight style. A term used by bird watchers to refer to a particular type of flight, such as hovering, which may be characteristic of a species.

flipper. The modified wings on penguins.

flock. A group of birds on land, in the water, or in flight.

flora. The vegetation of a particular geographic area.

flower-piercer. Various members of the family Coerebidae. The Indigo Flower-Piercer is an example.

flycatcher. A general name used to refer to various birds in the family Tyrannidae. The Eastern Kingbird is an example.

A Common Flicker at its nest. (Photo by Allan D. Cruickshank.)

A flock of Snow Geese at Brigantine National Wildlife Refuge, New Jersey.

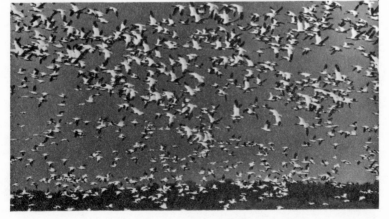

flyway. A term used mainly by waterfowl biologists to refer to broad areas of migration containing many individual migration routes of ducks, geese, and swans. In North America the four flyways used by waterfowl are the Atlantic, Mississippi, Central, and Pacific (see maps, pages 57-60). Occasionally the term also refers to narrow migration routes (see **flight line**), or short routes used by birds to fly between roosts and feeding areas.

foliage-gleaner. Various species in the family Furnariidae. The Rufous-rumped Foliage-Gleaner is an example.

food. The variety of plant or animal material consumed by birds is enormous and sometimes of major economic importance to man. Thus some birds eat carrion, many birds of prey eat large numbers of rodents, some songbirds consume impressive numbers of insects, cormorants and various seabirds eat fish of many species, and many sparrows eat seeds among other items. Seasonal and geographic considerations also influence the food which birds eat.

Forbush, Edward Howe (1858-1929). A celebrated State Ornithologist of Massachusetts who wrote many articles and books. He is best remembered for his monumental three-volume work *Birds of Massachusetts and Other New England States.*

forehead. On a bird, that forward part of a bird's head between the bill's base and the crown.

forest-falcon. The general name applied to several species in the family Falconidae. The Barred Forest-Falcon is an example.

form. A term used by taxonomists and bird watchers to refer to a "species" whose exact status in the process of avian classification is not certain.

Formicariidae. The antbird family.

Forster, Johann Reinhold (1729-1798). An ornithologist on Captain Cook's global voyage and the author of a work on the birds of Hudson Bay. Forster's Tern is named in his honor.

Fracé, Charles Lewis (1926-   ). A celebrated American wildlife artist whose paintings appear in leading conservation

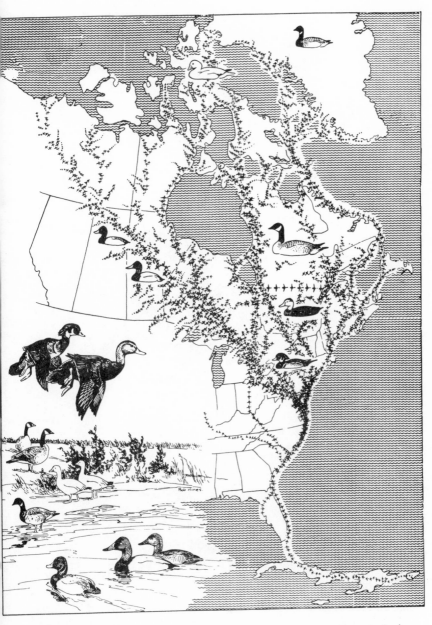

The Atlantic Flyway, showing the general routes used by migrating waterfowl. (Map courtesy of the United States Fish and Wildlife Service.)

The Mississippi Flyway, showing the general routes used by migrating waterfowl. (Map courtesy of the United States Fish and Wildlife Service.)

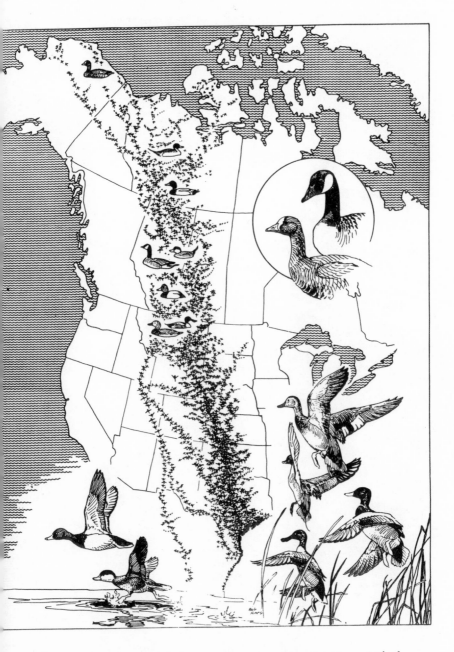

The Central Flyway, showing the general routes used by migrating waterfowl. (Map courtesy of the United States Fish and Wildlife Service.)

The Pacific Flyway, showing the general routes used by migrating waterfowl. (Map courtesy of the United States Fish and Wildlife Service.)

magazines. He also has illustrated numerous books, including *The Life of the Jungle, Animals in Action*, and *The Wolf*.

Franklin, Sir John (1786-1847). A British explorer who disappeared on an expedition in the Arctic. Franklin's Gull is named in his honor.

Fregatidae. The frigatebird family.

frigatebird. A term used to refer to one or more species in the family Fregatidae. The Great Frigatebird is an example.

Great Frigatebirds at nests on Tower Island, Galapagos.

Frigillidae. The finch family. Included are sparrows, grosbeaks, and related species.

frontal. Refers to the forehead of a bird.

Frost Bird. A local name for the American Golden Plover.

fruitcrow. A general term used to refer to several species in the family Cotingidae. The Crimson Fruitcrow is an example.

fruiteater. Various members of the family Cotingidae. The Handsome Fruiteater is an example.

61

Fuertes, Louis Agassiz (1874-1927). The most celebrated of modern American bird artists. He had a genius for capturing the spirit of living birds in his paintings. He illustrated numerous major books, including Eaton's *Birds of New York* and Forbush's *Birds of Massachusetts and Other New England States*.

fulmar. Refers to some species in the family Procellariidae. The Antarctic Petrel is an example.

furnariidae. The ovenbird family.

gaggle. Refers to a flock of geese on the ground or in water, but not in flight.

Galapagos Finch. See Darwin's Finch.

Galbulidae. The jacamar family.

Galliformes. The order containing the curassows, grouse, pheasants, turkeys, and the Hoatzin.

gallinaceous. Refers to grouse, pheasants, quail, and related species in the order Galliformes.

gallinule. Refers to several species of rail-like birds in the family Rallidae. The Purple Gallinule is an example.

Gambel, William (1819-1849). An early ornithologist who collected birds in California. The Gambel's Quail is named in his honor.

game bird. A term used by bird watchers and hunters to refer to species which can be hunted legally. Some examples are geese, ducks, grouse, pheasants, rails, and snipe.

A Northern Gannet on its nest on Bonaventure Island, Quebec.

gander. A male goose.

gannet. A general term used to refer to one or more members of the family Sulidae. In North America the term is used to refer to the Northern Gannet.

Gaviidae. The family containing the loons. The Common Loon is an example.

Gaviiformes. The order containing the family of loons.

geese. The plural form of "goose."

genera. The plural form of "genus."

genus. A taxonomic category which contains a single species or a group of closely related species of common evolutionary origin. In the Linnaean system of binomial nomenclature the scientific name of a bird contains first the name of the genus followed by the name of the species. Thus *Falco sparverius* is the scientific name of the American Kestrel. *Falco* is the name of the genus, *sparverius* the name of the species.

geographic distribution. The dispersal of something, such as a bird species, over an area of land such as a country or continent. The term also can be used for smaller areas.

geographic variation. The manner in which a species of bird or other animal varies in size, color, or other characteristics throughout different parts of its geographic range. Some birds show extensive geographic variation, others little or none.

Gilbert, Albert Earl (1939-   ). A well-known American bird and wildlife artist whose painting of a male Hooded Merganser was featured on the 1978 federal duck stamp. His drawings and paitings also are featured in many books, including *Eagles, Hawks and Falcons of the World*, *Handbook of New Guinea Birds*, and *Curassows and Related Birds*.

Gillespie, John A. (1893-1956). A past president of the Delaware Valley Ornithological Club and a student of Ospreys and Barn Owls.

Gilliard, E. Thomas (1912-1965). A widely celebrated and admired American ornithologist at the American Museum of Natural History. He is best known for his monumental studies of the birds of New Guinea. American bird watchers will best remember him for his splendid *Living Birds of the World* and various popular articles published in *National Geographic* magazine.

glide. A manner of flight in which no flapping of the wings is used.

gnatcatcher. Several small insect-eating species of birds in the the family Sylviidae. The Masked Gnatcatcher is an example.

gnateater. Several species in the family Formicariidae. The Rufous Gnateater is an example.

gnatwren. Several small species in the family Sylviidae. The Collared Gnatwren is an example.

godwit. Several species of shorebirds in the family Scolopacidae. The Hudsonian Godwit is an example.

A Marbled Godwit. (Photo by Dustin Huntington.)

goldfinch. Several species of finchlike birds in the family Fringillidae. The American Goldfinch is an example.

gonad. A sexual or reproductive organ. In males the gonads are called testes; in females they are called ovaries. In birds they become enlarged during the breeding season, then regress in size after the season is completed.

Goosander. A British term, rarely used in North America, to refer to the Common Merganser.

goose. A general term used to refer to various species of large waterfowl of which the Canada Goose is an example. Geese are smaller than swans but larger than ducks. Some common North American species include the Canada Goose, Snow Goose, and White-fronted Goose.

Goose-bird. A local name for the Hudsonian Godwit:

Gos. A term used by hawk watchers to refer to a Northern Goshawk. The term is in common use at many eastern hawk migration lookouts.

An Emperor Goose in Alaska.
(Photo by Sigurd T. Olson/U.S. Fish and Wildlife Service.)

Canada Geese landing on a pond.

Goshawk. A term used widely to refer to the Northern Goshawk.

grackle. A general term used to refer to various species in the genus *Quiscalus* of the family Icteridae. The Common Grackle is an example.

grassquit. Various members of the family Fringillidae. The Sooty Grassquit is an example.

Gray Coot. A local name for the Surf Scoter.

Gray Duck. Another name for the Mallard (both sexes). Also used locally for the Gadwall.

graytail. Several species in the family Furnariidae. The Equatorial Graytail is an example.

Greathead. The Common Goldeneye.

grebe. A general term used to refer to various species in the family Podicipedidae. The Horned Grebe is an example.

A Horned Grebe. (Photo by Allan D. Cruickshank.)

Green-head. A local name for the Mallard.

greenlet. Various species in the family Vireonidae. The Golden-fronted Greenlet is an example.

Green Plover. A local name for the American Golden Plover.

Green-wing. A name sometimes given to the Green-winged Teal.

George Bird Grinnell, a celebrated American ornithologist whose contributions to ornithology, conservation, and ethnology were profound. (Courtesy of the Smithsonian Archives, AOU Records.)

Grinnell, George Bird (1849-1938). A celebrated American ornithologist and ethnologist whose contributions to wildlife conservation were extensive and profound. He was a co-founder (with Theodore Roosevelt and others) of the famed Boone and Crockett Club, the New York Zoological Society, and numerous other noted organizations. He originated the idea for the creation of Glacier National Park and played a major role in its establishment. He also played an important role in the founding of Yellowstone National Park. He was vigorous in his defense of American Indians, especially the Blackfeet, and made major contributions to their welfare and even their survival. He lived among them for a period, learned their customs and language, and fought for their rights. When a student, as a young boy, he studied under Lucy Audubon—John James Audubon's wife. Thus he was a direct link with the early American ornithologists and naturalists who built the foundation for American natural history.

Grinnell, Joseph (1877-   ). A distinguished American ornithologist and the first director of the Museum of Vertebrate Zoology at the University of California. He wrote extensively about the birdlife of California and the West Coast.

grinning patch. The shape and coloration along the sides of the bills of some species of waterfowl, such as the Snow Goose, which give one the visual impression that the bird is grinning.

Griscom, Ludlow (1890-1959). A famous American ornithologist often considered the dean of bird watchers. He perfected the technique of sight identification of wild birds using binoculars. One of his important early books was *Birds of the New York City Region*.

grosbeak. A general term used to refer to certain species in the family Fringillidae. The Evening Grosbeak is an example.

An Evening Grosbeak at a bird feeder.
(Photo by Allan D. Cruickshank.)

Gross, Alfred Otto (1883-1970). An ornithologist of wide recognition who taught at Bowdoin College and was director of the Bowdoin Scientific Station on Kent Island. He wrote about many species of birds, including the Black-crowned Night Heron, Common Nighthawk, Heath Hen, Herring Gull, Snowy Owl, and many others.

ground-cuckoo. Several species in the family Cuculidae. The Scaled Ground-Cuckoo is an example.

ground-dove. Various smaller species in the family Columbidae. The Ruddy Ground-Dove is an example.

ground-tyrant. Various flycatcher species, of which the Puna Ground-Tyrant is an example.

grouse. A term used to refer to game birds in the family Tetrannidae. The Ruffed Grouse is an example.

Gruidae. The crane family.

Gruiformes. A large order of birds containing such families as cranes, limpkins, trumpeters, rails, finfoots, and sunbitterns.

An adult Herring Gull along the Maine coast.

71

Guacharo. A vernacular name sometimes given to the Oilbird.

guan. A general name of some of the species in the family Cracidae. The Andean Guan is an example.

guano. The accumulation of bird excrement such as one finds on islands off the coast of Peru on which large numbers of cormorants and other seabirds nest. Guano makes an excellent natural fertilizer for agricultural purposes, and it is mined for commercial sale on the Peruvian bird islands.

guide. See **field guide**.

gull. Various members of the subfamily Larinae. The Herring Gull is an example.

gullery. A colony of nesting gulls.

gullet. The anterior portion of a bird's esophagus.

gut. A bird's alimentary tract.

habitat. The natural area where a species of bird or other form of wildlife lives. A forest is an example. Some species have breeding habitats which are different from their feeding habitats. Winter habitats also are often different from the summer or spring habitats in which a species nests.

hack. The semi-freedom experienced by a newly fledgèd hawk or other bird of prey during which it flies over an area but returns to a site for food, often provided by a falconer or raptor manager.

hackle. The feathers on the nape of a bird.

hack station. A special station constructed for use by captively raised Peregrine Falcons, or other birds of prey, at which the young birds learn to feed and adapt to conditions in the wild as part of their release by raptor managers. A hack station may consist of a tower for use by the birds and an observation center located within telescope and binocular observation distance from the tower. Not all hack stations have observation centers, however.

The observation center at a Peregrine Falcon hack station in New Jersey.

Haematopodidae. The oystercatcher family.

Hairy Crown. Another name for the Hooded Merganser.

Hairy Head. A local name for the Hooded Merganser.

Hammond, William Alexander (1828-1900). A surgeon-general of the United States Army who conducted field studies of animals in the west. Hammond's Flycatcher is named in his honor.

Harlan, Richard (1796-1843). An early naturalist and physician who wrote the *Fauna Americana*. Harlan's Hawk (now a subspecies of the Red-tailed Hawk) honors his name.

Harlow, Richard C. (1889-1962). A celebrated American ornithologist and Curator of Oology at the Museum of Comparative Zoology at Harvard University. He also was elected to the Football Hall of Fame.

Harper, Francis (1886-1972). A well-known New England naturalist who made numerous and varied contributions to ornithology, mammalogy, natural history, and history.

harrier. A common term used to refer to members of the hawk genus *Circus*. The term is more popular in Europe, but it is beginning to come into use in North America. Thus the Marsh Hawk now is called the Northern Harrier.

Harris, Edward (1799-1863). A friend and companion of John James Audubon. Harris' Hawk honors his name.

hatch. The process whereby a young bird breaks out of its egg.

hatchling. A young bird which has just hatched.

hawk. In North America the term generally applies to the soaring hawks in the genus *Buteo*, or the bird-eating hawks in the genus *Accipiter*. However, the term also is applied frequently to any diurnal bird of prey except vultures and eagles. The Cooper's Hawk is an example.

hawk-eagle. A name given to the large eagles in the genera *Hieraaetus*, *Spizaetus*, and related genera.

hawking. See **falconry**.

hawk lookout. See **lookout**.

hawk watcher. A person who has a special interest in looking at diurnal birds of prey in the world. Most hawk watchers focus their efforts on spring and/or autumn hawk migrations,

A Northern Harrier (Marsh Hawk) in flight. (Photo by Fred Tilly.)

but some people also include in their activities observations of hawks during other seasons of the year.

hawk watching. The recreational hobby of looking at diurnal birds of prey, especially hawks migrating past natural concentration points. There also are a few professional ornithologists who focus their efforts into hawk-watching activities.

An adult female Rough-legged Hawk in flight. This species is a member of the genus Buteo. *(Photo by Fred Tilly.)*

head. The anterior or forward part of an animal's body. A bird's head includes the brain, eyes, ears, bill, and mouth.

Heath Hen. An extinct subspecies of the Greater Prairie Chicken.

Heermann, Adolphus L. (1818-1865). An early naturalist on the Pacific Railroad Survey of 1853-1854. He coined the term "oology," meaning the scientific study of bird eggs. Heermann's Gull is named in his honor.

Heliornithidae. The finfoot family.

Hell Diver. A name sometimes given to the Pied-billed Grebe.

hemispingus. Various species of tanagers. The Drab Hemispingus is an example.

hen. A term applied to a female bird, especially by hunters to game birds.

Hen Curlew. A local name for the Long-billed Curlew.

Henshaw, Henry Wetherbee (1850-1930). A celebrated American ethnologist and ornithologist who served as chief of the Biological Survey, a forerunner of the United States Fish and Wildlife Service. He was an important wildlife conservationist.

Henslow, John Stevens (1796-1861). A friend of John James Audubon and professor of botany at Cambridge University. Henslow's Sparrow is named in his honor.

hermit. Refers to certain species of forest-loving hummingbirds in the tropics. The Long-tailed Hermit is an example.

heron. A term sometimes applied to various species of waterbirds in the family Ardeidae. The Great Blue Heron is an example.

A Great Blue Heron.
(Photo by Allan D. Cruickshank.)

Hill Grass-bird. A local name for the Buff-breasted Sandpiper.

hillstar. Refers to certain species of hummingbirds. The Andean Hillstar is an example.

Hirundinidae. The swallow family.

Holarctic. Used by bird watchers and ornithologists to refer to the northern-hemisphere portions of the Old and New Worlds. The Old World portion is known as the Palaearctic and the New World portion as the Nearctic.

honeycreeper. Refers to various species of small tropical birds in the subfamily Coerebinae. The Red-legged Honeycreeper is an example. There also is a family of birds (Drepanididae) endemic to the Hawaiian Islands known as honeycreepers.

Honker. A term often used by American hunters to refer to the Canada Goose.

hood. A large and distinctive pattern of plumage covering much of the head of some species of birds. The Hooded Merganser is an example. Also a leather cap placed over the head and eyes of a hawk or falcon by falconers.

A male Ruby-throated Hummingbird at a sugar-water feeder.

Hooded Sheldrake. Another name for the Hooded Merganser.

hoot. Sometimes applied to the calls of various species of owls such as the Great Horned Owl.

hornero. Various species in the family Furnariidae. The Rufous Hornero is an example.

hover. A style of flight in which a bird remains more or less at one spot in midair while rapidly beating its wings. Various species of birds hover from time to time, including the Rough-legged Hawk, American Kestrel, and Eastern Kingbird.

Howell, Arthur H. (1872-1940). A well-known ornithologist best remembered for *Birds of Arkansas*, *Birds of Alabama*, and *Florida Bird Life*.

huet-huet. Several species in the family Rhinocryptidae. The Black-throated Huet-Huet is an example.

hummingbird. A general name applied to many species of beautiful birds in the family Trochilidae. Hummingbirds are native to the Americas. They are tiny birds known for their brilliant metallic colors and spectacular hovering flight, which produces a humming sound. The largest number of species occur in the American tropics.

hurricane bird. A bird, usually a seabird, carried into an area (such as North America) far from its normal geographic range by a hurricane. Generally such birds are trapped in the eye or vortex or a hurricane and thus move along with the path followed by the storm.

Hutton, William (dates unknown). An obscure bird collector who visited California in 1847-48. Hutton's Vireo is named in his honor.

hybrid. A bird which has resulted from the interbreeding of two different species. Hybrids show some of the physical and genetic characteristics of both parents. In general, hybrids are rare. However, among some families of birds, particularly waterfowl, they occur fairly commonly.

Hydrobatidae. The family containing the storm petrels. The Wilson's Storm Petrel is an example.

ibis. A general name applied to birds in the subfamily Thres-kiornithinae. The Scarlet Ibis is an example. *The Ibis* is the name of the journal published by the British Ornithologists' Union.

ice-bird. A vernacular name sometimes applied to prions of the the genus *Pachyptila*.

Icteridae. The family containing the New World blackbirds and orioles. The Red-winged Blackbird is an example.

inca. A general name applied to species of hummingbirds in the genus *Coeligena*. The Brown Inca is an example.

inca-finch. Several species in the family Fringillidae. The Great Inca-Finch is an example.

incubation. The process by which a bird, usually the female, sits on its eggs and transfers heat from its body to keep the eggs warm during the embryonic development of the young bird inside the egg.

interbreeding. The process by which a bird of one sex and spe-

A White Ibis. (Photo by Dustin Huntington.)

An American Robin on her nest incubating eggs.

cies mates with the opposite sex of another species. An example would be the interbreeding of a Mallard with an American Black Duck. See also **hybrid**.

invasion. Used by bird watchers and ornithologists to refer to an unusually large and unexpected movement of large numbers of birds into a geographic area which otherwise is devoid of the species or supports only a very limited number of individuals of the species. An example is the southward invasion about every four years of Snowy Owls from the Arctic.

iris. An opaque and often brightly colored membrane in front of the lens of a bird's eye. By opening or closing, the iris controls the amount of light entering the eye.

irruption. See **invasion**.

jacamar. Various species of birds in the family Galbulidae. The Rufous-tailed Jacamar is an example.

jacana. Long-legged waterbirds in the family Jacanidae. The Wattled Jacana is an example.

Jacanidae. The family containing the jacanas.

jack. A male Merlin.

Jackass Penguin. The Magellanic Penguin.

Jack Curlew. A local name for the Wimbrel.

jacobin. A general name applied to several species of tropical hummingbirds. The White-necked Jacobin is an example.

Jacobs, Joseph A. (1917-1977). A past president of the Delaware Valley Ornithological Club. He was well known for his studies and banding of Ospreys along the New Jersey coast. His efforts helped scientists to document the effect of DDT on Ospreys and other birds of prey.

jaeger. A name applied to several species of skuas. The Pomarine Jaeger is an example.

Jaques, Francis Lee (1887-1969). A celebrated American wildlife artist known widely for his diorama backgrounds in museums. He also illustrated many books, including *Oceanic Birds of South America, The Geese Fly High,* and *Birds Across the Sky.*

jay. A name applied to various species in the family Corvidae. The Blue Jay is an example.

jerkin. A male Gyrfalcon.

jesses. Leather straps fastened to the legs of birds of prey by falconers.

Jewett, Stanley Gordon (1885-1955). An authority on the birds of the Pacific Northwest. Among his writings are *Birds of Oregon* and *Birds of Washington State.*

Johnsgard, Paul Austin (1931-   ). A noted American waterfowl and game-bird authority who specializes in waterfowl behavior. Among his books are *Handbook of Waterfowl Behavior, Waterfowl: Their Biology and Natural History, Waterfowl*

Joseph A. Jacobs at an Osprey nest along coastal New Jersey.

of North America, and *Ducks, Geese and Swans of the World.* Dr. Johnsgard is professor of zoology at the University of Nebraska.

Jones, Lynds (1865-1951). A well-known figure in American ornithology and ecology. In 1895, at Oberlin College, he taught the first ornithology course ever offered in an American college. In 1910 he introduced at Oberlin a field ecology course—also the first offered in the country. In 1922, he established at Oberlin a Department of Animal Ecology—again the first in the country! He was one of the founders of the Wilson Ornithological Club (now Society) and served as the first editor of *The Wilson Bulletin.* He wrote extensively about many aspects of birds. His *A Revised Catalogue of the Birds of Ohio* is a classic.

juvenal. A term applied to the stage of development of a very young bird's plumage.

juvenile. Refers to the age of a bird; a young bird.

A Blue Jay in flight.

Kalmbach, Edwin Richard (1884-1972). A celebrated American wildlife ecologist who made major contributions to our knowledge of waterfowl migrations and small game. He also was a well-known wildlife artist.

Kempton Eagle. A term used by some hawk watchers at Hawk Mountain Sanctuary, Pennsylvania, to refer to a Turkey Vulture. Kempton is a small town located a few miles from Hawk Mountain.

Kestrel. The British and European name for the species *Falco tinnunculus*. In the United States and Canada the term is sometimes used by bird watchers to refer to the American Kestrel (*Falco sparverius*). There also are other species of kestrels in Eurasia and Africa.

kettle. A term used by hawk watchers to describe a group of migrating hawks, usually Broad-winged Hawks or Swainson's Hawks, milling around inside a thermal. Kettles of Broad-winged Hawks are among the most spectacular sights during the migration seasons and are eagerly looked for by hawk watchers and other bird watchers. Occasionally other birds also form kettles in thermals.

kingbird. Refers to certain New World flycatchers in the genus *Tyrannus*. The Eastern Kingbird is an example.

kingfisher. Refers to species in the family Alcedinidae. The Belted Kingfisher is an example.

kinglet. Used by bird watchers to refer to species in the genus *Regulus*. The Golden-crowned Kinglet is an example.

Kirtland, Jared Potter (1793-1877). An Ohio physician and naturalist who was the founder of the Cleveland Medical College. Kirtland's Warbler is named in his honor.

kiskadee. Refers to various flycatchers in the genus *Pitangus*. The Great Kiskadee is an example.

A kettle, or flock, of migrating Broad-winged Hawks in a thermal over an eastern Pennsylvania mountain.

kite. Refers to various species of diurnal birds of prey in the subfamily Elaninae and Milvinae. The Snail Kite is an example.

Kittlitz, Friedrich Heinrich (1779-1874). An officer in the German navy who explored some of the Alaskan islands. Kittlitz's Murrelet honors his name.

kittiwake. Refers to two species of gulls. The Black-legged Kittiwake is an example.

knot. Several species of shorebirds in the family Scolopacidae. The Red Knot is an example.

Koepcke, Maria Emilie Anna von Miculicz-Radecki (1924-1971). A German ornithologist and resident of Peru who made major contributions to Peruvian ornithology. She is best known for *The Birds of the Department of Lima, Peru.*

An adult male Snail Kite in Florida. (Photo by Helen G. Cruickshank.)

lamella. A thin plate or membrane. There are lamellae located along the side of the bill of a duck.

lancebill. Hummingbirds in the genus *Doryfera*. The Blue-fronted Lancebill is an example.

Land, Hugh Colman (1929-1968). An American ornithologist and authority on the birds of Guatemala. He is best known for his book *Birds of Guatemala*.

Laniidae. The family containing the skrikes. The Northern Shrike is an example.

Lansdowne, James Fenwick (1937-   ). An internationally celebrated wildlife artist best known for his paintings in *Birds of the Northern Forest*, *Birds of the Eastern Forest*, *Birds of the West Coast*, and *Rails of the World*.

lapwing. Refers to shorebirds in the genus *Vanellus*. The Andean Lapwing is an example.

Laridae. The family containing the gulls and terns. Gulls are placed in the subfamily Larinae; terns belong to the subfamily Sterninae.

A Horned Lark at its nest.

lark. A general term for species in the family Alaudidae. The Horned Lark is an example.

Lawrence, George Newbold (1806-1895). One of the naturalists on the Pacific Railroad Surveys. Lawrence's Goldfinch honors his name.

layering. Refers to the height at which various species of birds, especially wood warblers, secure food or build their nests in forest vegetation. Different species occupy different layers or levels of vegetation from the ground to the crown of the forest.

LBJ. See **little brown job**.

Leach, William Elford (1790-1836). An English naturalist and specialist in shells and insects. Leach's Storm Petrel honors his name.

leading-line. See **diversion-line**.

leafscraper. Refers to several species in the family Furnariidae. The Gray-throated Leafscraper is an example.

LeConte, John (1818-1891). A physician and former president of the University of California at Berkeley. LeConte's Sparrow honors his name.

leg. The lower limb; a bird's leg is the tibiotarsus.

lesser coverts. See **coverts**.

Leitlinie. The German term for "leading-line." See **diversion-line**.

Lewis, Meriwether (1774-1809). A captain in the United States Army and one of the leaders of the Lewis and Clark Expedition. Lewis' Woodpecker is named in his honor.

life list. A written record of the names of the various species of wild birds one has seen during one's life. There are many types of life lists, including world lists, North American lists, state lists, regional lists, local lists, and others. Those bird watchers whose main concern is developing as large a bird life list as possible are sometimes called listers.

Limpkin. The sole member of the family Aramidae.

Lincoln, Frederick (1892-1960). A noted wildlife biologist and ornithologist with the United States Fish and Wildlife Service. He developed the Lincoln Index, used widely in wildlife management, and was co-author of *The Birds of Alaska*.

Lincoln, Thomas (1812-1883). A young friend of John James Audubon who joined the great naturalist on a trip to Labrador. Lincoln's Sparrow is named in his honor.

Lincoln Index. A formula used by wildlife bologists to calculate the approximate population of a species of bird or other animal living on a specific area.

Lindblad Explorer, **M. S.** A celebrated tourist exploration ship operated by Lindblad Travel, Inc., in New York City. Most bird watchers visiting the Antarctic, and certain other remote areas of the world, do so on board this famous and unique ship.

Linsdale, Jean Myron (1902-1969). An ornithologist from the University of California at Berkeley. He is perhaps known best for his teaching of graduate students and his *Game Birds of California*.

lister. A bird watcher who maintains a written record of all the species of birds he or she has observed, and whose main goal in bird watching is to add to the numbers of birds on his or her life. See **life list**.

Little Blackbreast. A local name for the Dunlin.

little brown job. Sometimes used to refer to various small brown birds which one may not be able to identify.

Little Loon. Another name for the Red-throated Loon.

Little Ring-neck. A local name for the Semipalmated Plover.

llano. A savanna-like habitat found in parts of South America.

Logcock. Another name for the Pileated Woodpecker.

Lloyd, Hoyes (1888-1978). A well-known bird conservationist.

The M.S. Lindblad Explorer *on which many bird watchers visit the Antarctic and other remote parts of the world.*

Long-billed Rail. A local name for the Virginia Rail.

Long-tail. A local name for the Oldsquaw.

long-winged hawks. A term sometimes used to refer to falcons.

lookout. A term generally used by hawk watchers to refer to the observation point from which they observe migrating diurnal birds of prey in spring or autumn. Hawk Mountain Sanctuary, Pennsylvania, is an example of such a lookout.

A hawk watcher on a mountain hawk lookout in eastern Pennsylvania.

Loomis, Leverett Mills (1857-1928). An American ornithologist from the California Academy of Sciences with a special interest in seabirds. He developed a major collection of these birds at the Academy and wrote many technical articles about them. He also played a key role in having the Farallon Islands declared a national wildlife refuge.

loon. Refers to the species in the family Gaviidae. The Red-throated Loon is an example.

loonatic. Bird watchers with a special interest in loons.

lore. The portion of the face of a bird between the eye and the upper mandible.

Low, Seth Haskell (1911-1962). A distinguished bird bander and wildlife biologist with the United States Fish and Wildlife Service. He is best known for his contribution to banding techniques and data analysis.

loop migration. Refers to bird migration routes that cross different geographic areas in spring and autumn, thus forming a loop or ellipse. The American Golden Plover uses migration loops.

Lucas, Frederick Augustus (1852-1929). An ornithologist and director of the American Museum of Natural History. He wrote extensively about birds. Lucas Glacier, on South Georgia, was named in his honor by Robert Cushman Murphy.

macaw. A name applied to certain species of very large parrots. The Blue-and-yellow Macaw is an example.

MacGillivray, William (1796-1852). A British ornithologist and anatomist who helped to correct some of John James Audubon's writings prior to publication. MacGillivray's Warbler is named in his honor.

magpie. Used by North American bird watchers to refer to several species in the family Corvidae. The Black-billed Magpie is an example.

manakin. A term applied to the species in the family Pipridae. The Blue-backed Manakin is an example.

mandible. The lower jaw.

mango. Refers to several species of hummingbirds in the genus *Anthracothorax*. The Green-throated Mango is an example.

man-o'-war bird. See **frigatebird**.

Marlin. A local name for the Marbled Godwit.

marshbird. Several species of Icterids. The Yellow-rumped Marshbird is an example.

Marsh-plover. A local name for the Pectoral Sandpiper.

martin. A general term applied to certain species in the family Hirundinidae. The Purple Martin is an example.

McAtee, W. L. (1883-1962). The dean of American economic ornithologists. He served with the United States Fish and Wildlife Service, and its early forerunners, for decades and made profound investigations into the food habits of birds. He also devoted attention to numerous other topics.

McCown, John P. (1815-1879). A captain in the United States Army and a naturalist. McCown's Longspur honors his name.

McKay, Charles Leslie (?-1883). A member of the Signal Corps and a naturalist who collected birds in Alaska. McKay's Bunting is named in his honor.

McLaughlin, Frank W. (1906-1977). An executive director of the New Jersey Audubon Society and a well-known bird conservationist.

Meadow Chicken. A local name for a Sora.

meadowlark. Refers to several species of Icterids in the genus *Sturnella*. The Eastern Meadowlark is an example.

melanistic. Black or intensely pigmented. Used by bird watchers to refer to black or very dark plumage on an individual bird whose species normally is colored much lighter. In some instances it also refers to a color phase of the plumage of some species.

Meleagrididae. The turkey family.

Meng, Heinz Karl (1924-   ). An internationally recognized expert on birds of prey. He is best known for his classic studies of the Cooper's Hawk and becoming the first person in North America to breed endangered Peregrine Falcons successfully in captivity. He now continues to breed Peregrines, and certain other birds of prey, at the New Paltz Peregrine Falcon Foundation.

merg. A bird watcher's term meaning "merganser."

merganser. Used to refer to several species of waterfowl in the genus *Mergus*. The Hooded Merganser is an example.

Heinz Meng feeding Peregrine Falcon chicks bred in captivity at the New Paltz Peregrine Falcon Foundation. (Photo courtesy of Heinz Meng.)

A male Hooded Merganser.

Merriam, Clinton Hart (1855-1942). A celebrated naturalist, ornithologist, and mammalogist. He co-founded the Division of Economic Ornithology and Mammalogy in the United States Department of Agriculture, and originated the concept of life zones in North America.

metaltail. Various hummingbird species. The Fire-throated Metaltail is an example.

mew. A building in which falconers house their trained hawks and falcons.

middle coverts. See **coverts**.

migration. The periodic movement of birds (or other animals) from one place to another. There are various types of migrations, the most common being daily and seasonal.

migration corridor. A concept developed by waterfowl biologist Frank C. Bellrose to express the direction of migration, and geographic distribution of waterfowl, moving between nesting and wintering grounds. Migration corridors are less extensive in geographic scope than the more traditional flyways used to describe waterfowl migrations in North America.

Miller, Alden Holmes (1906-1965). A director of the Museum of Vertebrate Zoology at the University of California at Berkeley. He published widely on various aspects of ornithology, including a classic monograph of the genus *Junco*. He also taught and served as administrator.

Miller, Loye Holmes (1874-1970). A celebrated expert on fossil birds and professor at the University of California at Berkeley.

Miller, Waldron De Witt (1879-1929). An ornithologist at the American Museum of Natural History with a wide interest in birds, particularly birds of prey. He was aware of the slaughter of migrating hawks at what is now Hawk Mountain, Pennsylvania, for some years prior to the establishment of that refuge.

Mimidae. The family containing the mockingbirds, thrashers, and related species. The Tropical Mockingbird is an example.

A Northern Mockingbird. (Photo by Luther C. Goldman/U.S. Fish and Wildlife Service.)

Smaller species of albatrosses, such as these Black-browed Albatrosses, are sometimes referred to as mollymauks.

miner. Various species in the family Furnariidae. The Grayish Miner is an example.

mist net. A very fine nylon net used by bird banders (under authority of state and federal permits) to capture birds for banding and/or marking purposes.

mockingbird. A general term used to refer to various species in the family Mimidae. The Northern Mockingbird is an example.

mollymauk. Used by sailors and bird watchers to refer to the smaller species of albatrosses. The Black-browed Albatross is an example.

99

molt. The natural periodic loss and replacement of the feathers of a bird.

Momotidae. The motmot family.

monjita. Several flycatchers, of which the White Monjita is an example.

monocular. An optical instrument, used with one eye, to magnify objects such as birds observed from a distance. A telescope.

moon watching. A technique invented by Dr. George Lowery at Louisiana State University whereby a telescope is focused on the surface of the moon at night in order to permit an observer to count the number of birds observed passing across the face of the moon. Such counts of passing birds provide ornithologists with a very crude index to the magnitude of bird migration on a given date.

Moore, Robert Thomas (1882-1958). An ornithologist best known for his *Distributional Check-list of the Birds of Mexico.*

morph. A British term used to refer to certain populations of a species which have differently colored plumage from other populations of the same species. Thus the term sometimes replaces use of the term "color phase" or "phase." For example, the blue color phase of the Snow Goose can be called the blue morph.

The blue color phase of the Snow Goose is known as a morph.

*Robert Cushman Murphy.
He was considered the greatest
of all students of seabirds.*

Motacillidae. The pipit family.

Mother Carey's chicken. Sailors have used the term to refer to various species of storm petrels in the family Hydrobatidae. The Wilson's Storm Petrel is an example.

motmot. A term used to refer to the species in the family Momotidae. The Blue-crowned Motmot is an example.

moult. See **molt**.

mountain-finch. Several species in the family Fringillidae. The Tucuman Mountain-Finch is an example.

mountain-gem. Refers to species of hummingbirds in the genus *Lampornis*. The Green-throated Mountain-Gem is an example. All mountain-gems are restricted to Central America.

mountain-tanager. Various species of tanagers. The Masked Mountain-Tanager is an example.

mourner. A name applied to certain species of cotingas.

Mud-Hen. A local name for the American Coot.

Mud-Peep. A local name for the Least Sandpiper.

Mud Sheldrake. Another name for the Hooded Merganser.

Mud Teal. A local name for the Green-winged Teal.

Murphy, Robert Cushman (1887-1973). An international authority on seabirds and former chairman of the Department of

Ornithology at the American Museum of Natural History. Among his books which are classics are *Oceanic Birds of South America, Logbook for Grace,* and *Bird Islands of Peru.* Murphy's Petrel is named in his honor.

murre. Refers to certain species in the family Alcidae. The Common Murre is an example.

murrelet. A name applied to certain species in the family Alcidae. The Marbled Murrelet is an example.

mutton-bird. A term sometimes applied to some species of seabirds. Examples are Short-tailed Shearwaters and Atlantic Petrels.

nail. On a duck, goose, or swan, the hornlike tip of the upper mandible.

nape. The back of the neck.

nares. The nostrils.

native. Breeding or otherwise occurring regularly in a particular geographic area.

natural history. The study of nature, including animals and plants. Most natural-history studies are descriptive rather than quantitative.

naturalist. A person who studies natural history.

Nearctic. Refers to North America north of the tropical rain-forests of Mexico.

neck. The portion of the anatomy between the head and body.

Neotropics. Refers to the tropical portions of the Americas, including the West Indies.

nest. The structure which a bird makes (in most instances) and in which it deposits its eggs. Not all species make nests.

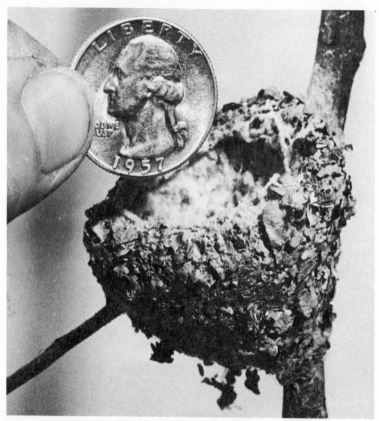

A Ruby-throated Hummingbird nest shown in comparison with a quarter.

nest box. A man-made bird house.

nestling. A young bird still in the nest.

Nest Record Program. A record-keeping program, using computers, operated by the Cornell University Laboratory of Ornithology in which volunteers gather details at the active nests of North American birds and forward the data to the laboratory for use in that institution's North American Nest Record Program.

Nice, Margaret Morse (1883-1974). A celebrated American ornithologist best known for her classic *Studies in the Life History of the Song Sparrow* and *Development of Behavior in Precocial Birds.*

niche. The role or activity that a bird engages in within the habitat in which it lives. A bird's niche is its profession or occupation. Thus a hawk is a predator, a vulture a scavenger.

nictitating membrane. The third eyelid which helps to protect a bird's eye.

nighthawk. Refers generally to New World species in the family Caprimulgidae. The Common Nighthawk is an example.

nightingale-thrush. Several species of tropical thrushes. The Orange-billed Nightingale-Thrush is an example.

A Wood Duck nest box. (Drawing courtesy of the U.S. Fish and Wildlife Service.)

Nestling Black-crowned Night Herons.

nightjar. Refers to various members of the family Caprimulgidae. The Rufous Nightjar is an example.

nocturnal. Active at night. Most owls are nocturnal.

noddy. Refers to several species of small terns. The Brown Noddy is an example.

North American Nest Record Program. See **Nest Record Program**.

nunbird. Several species in the family Bucconidae. The Black Nunbird is an example.

nunlet. Several species in the family Bucconidae. The Rusty-breasted Nunlet is an example.

nuptial plumage. The plumage worn by a bird during the breeding season.

nuthatch. Species in the family Sittidae. The White-breasted Nuthatch is an example.

Nuttall, Thomas (1786-1859). An English naturalist and ornithologist who settled for a period in the United States and later wrote *A Manual of the Ornithology of the United States and Canada*. Several species of birds honor him, including Nuttall's Woodpecker.

Nyctibiidae. The potoo family.

Oberholser, Harry Church (1870-1963). A celebrated ornithologist at the United States National Museum. He described 560 new species and subspecies of birds as well as many new genera, subfamilies, and families of birds. He wrote almost 900 technical articles as well as such classic books as *Bird Life of Louisiana* and *The Bird Life of Texas*.

observatory. A scientific research station devoted to bird study in a particular area. The observatory usually is staffed with trained professional ornithologists who are assisted by skilled amateur bird watchers, bird banders, and other interested persons. There usually is a well-equipped building at a bird observatory which serves as an office, laboratory, library, and center of research activity. Most bird observatories are located on important bird migration flyways or at other bird concentration points.

oceanic birds. Birds that live on the open oceans; pelagic birds.

Oilbird. A unique nightjar-like bird with a limited distribution in the American tropics. It is the only member of the family Steatornithidae.

Oilbirds on their nests in a Trinidad grotto.

oil gland. A gland, whose opening is located near the base of a bird's tail, from which the bird secures the protective oil it applies as waterproofing to its feathers.

Old Injun. A local name for the Oldsquaw.

Old Wife. A local name for the Oldsquaw.

O'Neill, John Patton (1942-   ). A well-known American bird and wildlife artist perhaps best known for his illustrations in books such as *Distribution of the Birds of Honduras, Grouse and Quails of North America,* and *A Guide to the Birds of Trinidad and Tobago.*

oologist. A person who collects bird eggs.

oology. The scientific study of bird eggs.

Opisthocomidae. The Hoatzin family.

oriole. Refers to various species in the family Icteridae. The Orchard Oriole is an example.

ornithologist. A scientist who studies birds.

ornithology. The scientific study of birds.

oropendola. Various tropical members of the family Icteridae. The Crested Oropendola is an example.

A nestling Osprey.

Osgood, Wilfred Hudson (1875-1947). A well-known mammalogist and ornithologist from the Field Museum in Chicago. He published widely on birds and mammals.

Osprey. A fish-eating hawk and the only member of the family Pandionidae. The species has a geographic distribution that is almost worldwide.

owl. Refers to nocturnal birds of prey in the order Strigiformes. The Great Horned Owl is an example.

owl prowl. An owl-watching technique used by some bird watchers to listen to, and observe, owls at night. One drives along rural roads and makes stops, at least three minutes in duration, at spots where owls are likely to be present. Generally a tape recording of Screech, Great Horned, Barred, or Saw-whet Owls is played to attract the attention of any owls in the area. Some owl watchers also whistle Screech Owl calls instead of using a tape recorder. Not infrequently owls not only respond vocally but also fly close to the observer, who then observes and studies the birds by moonlight or in

110

the bright beam of a flashlight. Owl prowls are excellent ways in which to census local owl populations. They also can be useful in introducing students to the world of owls.

owl watcher. A bird watcher with a special interest in observing and studying owls.

Oxyruncidae. The sharpbill family.

oystercatcher. Refers to shorebirds in the family Haematopodidae. The American Oystercatcher is an example.

A Saw-whet Owl. (Photo by Allan D. Cruickshank.)

pack. A flock (larger than a covey) of grouse.

Painted Goose. Refers to the Emperor Goose.

pair bond. Refers to a special relationship between a male and female of the same species especially for breeding purposes. There is enormous variation in the types and lengths of pair bonds among various species of birds.

Palmer, Theodore Sherman (1868-1955). A well-known naturalist, ornithologist, and wildlife conservationist who helped secure early bird-protection laws in the United States.

pampa-finch. Several species in the family Fringillidae. The Great Pampa-Finch is an example.

pampas. Prairielike habitats in parts of South America.

Pandionidae. The Osprey family.

parakeet. Small species in the family Psittacidae. The Golden Parakeet is an example.

Paridae. The family containing chickadees and titmice.

Parnall, Peter (1936-   ). A widely known American wildlife artist best known for his illustrations in *The Nightwatchers*, *Four Winds*, and *The Mountain*.

parrot. Refers to various species in the family Psittacidae. The Blue-headed Parrot is an example.

Parulidae. The New World wood warbler family.

parulids. Species of wood warblers in the family Parulidae. The Yellow Warbler is an example.

Passeriformes. The huge order of perching birds containing about one-half of the world's species of birds. Most of these species are known commonly as songbirds.

passerine. Of or relating to the order Passeriformes.

pelagic. Oceanic; refers to species of birds such as albatrosses, petrels, shearwaters, and storm petrels.

An immature Brown Pelican.

pelagic wandering. Refers to nomadic wanderings of pelagic birds over the oceans and seas of the world.

Pelecanidae. The family containing the pelicans.

Pelecaniformes. The order containing the tropicbirds, pelicans, boobies, cormorants, anhingas, and frigatebirds.

Pelecanoididae. The family containing the diving petrels.

pelican. Member of the family Pelecanidae. The Brown Pelican is an example.

pellet. A compact mass of undigested bones, fur, feathers, insect remains, and similar materials ejected orally by an owl, hawk, or occasionally certain other species of birds. Owl pellets are extremely important to researchers in helping them to determine what these birds eat.

pen. A female swan.

penguin. Refers to birds of the family Spheniscidae. The King Penguin is an example.

A colony of King Penguins on the island of South Georgia in the Antarctic.

peppershrike. Several species in the family Vireonidae. The Rufous-browed Peppershrike is an example.

permanent resident. A species of bird that remains in a particular geographic area throughout the year. It does not migrate but may roam short distances in the area in which it is found.

Peters, James Lee (1889-1952). An international authority on bird classification best known for his monumental *Checklists of Birds of the World*.

Peterson. Refers to Roger Tory Peterson's various field guides to bird identification. Thus when a person states that he or she is referring to his or her Peterson, it is meant that reference is being made to *A Field Guide to the Birds* or another of Dr. Peterson's popular books.

Peterson, Roger Tory (1908-   ). An internationally celebrated bird artist, photographer, and author of the classic *A Field Guide to the Birds*, which launched the modern era of bird

Roger Tory Peterson in his Connecticut studio.
(Photo courtesy of Roger Tory Peterson.)

watching. His influence upon bird watching, and nature study generally, is enormous because of his development of the concept of modern field guides. He wrote many other books, after his classic eastern bird guide, including *A Field Guide to Western Birds*, *A Field Guide to Mexican Birds*, *A Field Guide to Wild Flowers*, *The World of Birds*, *Wild America*, and others. He also is a major wildlife conservationist whose influence extends around the globe.

petrel. Refers to various seabirds in the family Procellariidae. The Kermadec Petrel is an example.

Pettingill, Olin Sewall, Jr. (1907-   ). A celebrated American ornithologist and wildlife photographer, a former director of the Cornell Laboratory of Ornithology, and the author of *A Guide to Bird Finding East of the Mississippi* and *A Guide to Bird Finding West of the Mississippi*. His textbook *Ornithology in Laboratory and Field* is used widely in American colleges and universities, and his popular book *Another Penguin Summer* is a charming account of the penguins of the Falkland Islands. He also is known widely as a wildlife film lecturer. He has made motion pictures released by Walt Disney.

Olin Sewall Pettingill, Jr., at a King Penguin colony in the Antarctic. (Photo by Eleanor Rice Pettingill.)

pewee. Several species of flycatchers. The Greater Pewee is an example.

Phaethontidae. The family containing the tropicbirds.

Phalacrocoracidae. The cormorant family.

phalarope. Refers to three small shorebirds in the family Phalaropodidae. The Red Phalarope is an example.

Phalaropodidae. The phalarope family.

phase. A color variation, usually light or tan, exhibited by some species of birds.

Phasianidae. The pheasant family.

pheasant. Various large species in the family Phasianidae. The Ring-necked Pheasant is an example.

Pheasant Duck. A hunters name, used locally, for the Common Pintail.

Phelps, William Henry (1875-1965). A celebrated ornithologist and authority on the birds of Venezuela. He developed an important collection of Venezuelan birds—the Collection Ornithologica Phelps in Caracas. His major books include *Lista de las Aves de Venezuela con su Distribución Geográfica.*

Phillips, John Charles (1876-1938). A physician and ornithologist well known for his studies of waterfowl. His four-volume *A Natural History of the Ducks* is monumental in the literature of waterfowl.

phoebe. Refers to several flycatchers in the genus *Sayornis*. The Eastern Phoebe is an example.

Phoenicopteridae. The flamingo family.

Phytotomidae. The plantcutter family.

Picidae. The woodpecker family.

Piciformes. The order containing the jacamars, puffbirds, barbets, honeyguides, toucans, woodpeckers, and wrynecks.

Picket-tail. Another name for the Common Pintail.

piculet. A name applied to various primitive woodpecker species. The Chestnut Piculet is an example.

piedtail. Several tropical species of hummingbirds. The Peruvian Piedtail is an example.

Pied-wing Curlew. A local name for the Willet.

Pigeon. Used by some bird watchers to refer to the Rock Dove. Alternatively, refers generally to the various larger dovelike birds in the family Columbidae. The Plumbeous Pigeon is an example.

piha. Various species in the family Cotingidae. The Screaming Piha is an example.

pinion. Sometimes used to refer to a bird's wing, or part of the wing such as a primary feather.

pinnated. Feathered; however, the terms refers especially to birds, such as the Greater Prairie Chicken, that have elongated, winglike tufts of feathers on the side of the neck.

pioneering spirit. The willingness, or lack thereof, of individuals of a species to venture into and use geographic areas seldom or never used previously.

Pintail. Commonly used to refer to the Common Pintail.

piping-guan. Refers to several species in the family Cracidae. The Red-throated Piping-Guan is an example.

pipit. Birds in the family Motacillidae. The Water Pipit is an example.

Pipridae. The family containing the manakins.

pitta. Refers generally to various species in the family Pittidae.

Pittidae. The family containing the pittas.

plantcutter. A name applied to three species of South American birds in the family Phytotomidae. The Peruvian Plantcutter is an example.

Ploceidae. The family containing the weaverbirds.

plover. Refers to various species of shorebirds in the family

Charadriidae. The Piping Plover is an example.

plumage. The feathers covering a bird.

plumeleteer. Refers to several tropical species of humming-birds. The Bronze-tailed Plumeleteer is an example.

Podicipedidae. The family containing the grebes.

Podicipediformes. The order containing the grebes.

polytypic. Having more than one type of subdivision; refers to a species that is separated into two or more subspecies.

Poole, Earl Lincoln (1891-1972). A director of the Reading Public Museum and Art Gallery in Reading, Pennsylvania, and a noted ornithologist, mammalogist, and wildlife artist. He illustrated various books and wrote several of his own, including *Pennsylvania Birds*.

potoo. A name applied to various species of nighthawk-like birds in the family Nyctibiidae. The species live in Central and South America. The Common Potoo is an example.

prairie. A North American plain without trees but covered with grass.

prairie chicken. Refers to several species of grouselike game birds in the genus *Tympanuchus*. The Greater Prairie Chicken is an example.

precocial. Active from birth. The term is applied to birds that are at once active and depart from the nest after hatching. A duckling is an example.

predation. The killing of an animal by another animal for food. The animal killed is the prey; the animal doing the killing is the predator.

predator. A bird, or other animal, that secures its food by capturing, killing, and eating other animals. Hawks and owls are avian predators.

preen. The process by which birds smooth feathers on their body that become ruffled by using their bills to place the feathers back into the correct arrangement. During the preen-

A Canada Goose preening its feathers.

ing process, oil from the bird's oil gland (in most species) sometimes is applied with the bill to the feathers to water-proof them.

preen gland. See **oil gland.**

prey. An animal or species of animal that is killed by a predator.

primary. One of the main flight feathers on a bird's wing.

primary coverts. See **coverts.**

prion. A seabird of the genus *Pachyptila*. The Slender-billed Prion is an example.

Procellariidae. The family containing the shearwaters and true petrels.

Procellariiformes. The order of seabirds or tubenoses, *i.e.*, albatrosses, shearwaters, petrels, storm petrels, and diving petrels.

Psittacidae. The parrot family.

Psittaciformes. The order containing the parrots.

Psophiidae. The trumpeter family.

ptarmigan. Refers to grouselike birds of the genus *Lagopus*. The Willow Ptarmigan is an example.

Ptilogonatidae. The silky-flycatcher family.

puffbird. Various birds in the family Bucconidae. The White-necked Puffbird is an example.

puffin. Refers to several species in the family Alcidae. The Atlantic Puffin is an example.

A Common (Atlantic) Puffin carrying fish in its bill. (Photo by Allan D. Cruickshank.)

121

puffleg. Refers to hummingbirds of the genus *Eriocnemis*. The Glowing Puffleg is an example.

pupil. The opening in the iris of an eye.

purpletuft. Several species in the family Cotingidae. The Dusky Purpletuft is an example.

pygmy-owl. Several small species of owls, some of which are distributed widely in the tropics. The Ferruginous Pygmy-Owl is an example.

pygmy-tyrant. Various species of flycatchers. The Eared Pygmy-Tyrant is an example.

quail. Refers to various game birds in the family Phasianidae. The Bobwhite is an example.

quail-dove. Various species in the family Columbidae. The Ruddy Quail-Dove is an example.

quetzal. A name applied to several species of trogans. The Resplendent Quetzal is an example.

quill. The shaft of a feather. Also, a major wing or tail feather.

race. A term used by ornithologists, and some bird watchers, to refer to a subspecies of bird.

radar ornithology. The scientific study of bird migration via the use of radar to follow or track the movements of birds. The techniques are sophisticated and generally are used by professional ornithologists only.

raft. A flock of ducks, such as eiders, resting on the water. The term frequently refers to flocks of diving ducks.

Raft Duck. The Lesser Scaup.

rail. A name applied generally to birds in the family Rallidae. The Sora is an example.

rain forest. Refers to various types of lush tropical forests which are subject to torrential rains during various seasons of the year. There also are temperate rain forests.

Rallidae. The family containing the rails.

Ramphastidae. The family containing the toucans.

range. The geographic area occupied by a species of bird or other animal or plant.

raptor. A diurnal or nocturnal birds of prey such as a hawk or owl.

Raptores. An obsolete name formerly given to the order containing the diurnal birds of prey. The birds now are placed in the order Falconiformes. The term also is used occasionally to mean all of the birds of prey (hawks and owls). Thus the raptores are predatory birds.

raptor rehabilitation. The care of injured birds of prey, in spe-

The Sora is one of various species of rails in North America.

125

cial facilities, with the objective being the eventual return of such birds to the wild. Raptor rehabilitation is conducted under authority of special state and federal permits.

Rare Bird Alert. A recorded message on a tape recorder connected to a telephone. The message contains details about unusual or rare birds seen in a particular geographic area. A person simply dials the telephone number of the RBA and listens to the recorded message. Rare Bird Alerts usually are used in the larger cities in the United States. Such RBA messages generally are updated about once a week by the bird club or organization providing the service.

RBA. See **Rare Bird Alert**.

recovery plan. A plan of action, based upon research, by which wildlife biologists propose to try to save endangered species of wildlife from extinction and to cause the species to increase their numbers to such a point that they no longer are considered endangered. The United States Fish and Wildlife Service is responsible for the final approval of all recovery plans designed for use on federally listed endangered species. Eventually each endangered species will have a recovery plan designed for its peculiar needs.

rectrices. The tail feathers of a bird.

Recurvirostridae. The family of shorebirds containing the stilts and avocets.

Redback. A local name for the Dunlin.

Red-breasted Plover. A local name for the Red Knot.

red-cotinga. Several species in the family Cotingidae. The Guianian Red-Cotinga is an example.

Red Curlew. A local name for the Marbled Godwit.

Red List. A list of endangered species.

redpoll. Certain species in the family Fringillidae. The Common Redpoll is an example.

Red-shoulder. A term used by some hawk watchers to refer to the Red-shouldered Hawk.

*A view of the boardwalk in Great Swamp
National Wildlife Refuge, New Jersey.*

redstart. Various species of wood warblers. The American Redstart is an example.

Red-tail. A term used commonly by hawk watchers to refer to a
Red-tailed Hawk.

Reece, Maynard (1920-   ). A celebrated American bird and
wildlife artist perhaps best known for his paintings of waterfowl. Five different federal duck stamps have featured
his waterfowl paintings over the years. Various books also
contain his illustrations.

reedhaunter. Several species in the family Furnariidae. The
Straight-billed Reedhaunter is an example.

refuge. A wildlife sanctuary. The United States Fish and Wildlife Service owns and operates hundreds of wildlife refuges

throughout the United States. In addition, there are state, local, and private refuges. All are important because they preserve vital bird habitat.

remiges. The primary and secondary feathers on a bird's wing.

reverse migration. Refers to birds that are moving in the direction opposite from which they should be moving during the spring or autumn migration seasons. Reverse migration sometimes is caused by a temporary change in weather or wind direction.

rhea. Refers to two South American species in the family Rheidae.

Rheidae. The family containing the rheas.

Rheiformes. The order containing the rheas.

Rhinocryptidae. The tapaculo family.

Rhoads, Samuel Nicholson (1863-1952). A celebrated ornithologist, mammalogist, and naturalist who described numerous species and subspecies of birds and mammals. He was one of the founders of the Delaware Valley Ornithological Club. His book *The Mammals of Pennsylvania and New Jersey* is a classic.

Robert Ridgway. (Photo courtesy Smithsonian Archives.)

Ridgway, Robert (1850-1929). A major American ornithologist on the staff of the Smithsonian Institution. He was an avian taxonomist of enormous importance and one of the founders of the American Ornithologists' Union. He is best known for his monumental multivolume work *Birds of North and Middle America*.

Ring-billed Duck. Another name for the Ring-necked Duck.

ringing. A British term meaning bird banding.

Ring-neck. A local name for the Piping Plover.

Ring-necked Scaup. A local name for the Ring-necked Duck.

Ring-tailed Marlin. A local name for the Hudsonian Godwit.

Ripley, Sidney Dillon (1913-   ). An internationally celebrated ornithologist and the current secretary of the Smithsonian Institution. He is an authority on waterfowl, rails, and the birds of the Indian subcontinent. He also is a noted wildlife conservationist, explorer, and art connoisseur. Among his books are *A Paddling of Ducks*, *Handbook of the Birds of India and Pakistan*, and *Rails of the World*.

River Broad-bill. The Lesser Scaup.

Robbins, Chandler Seymour (1918-   ). A celebrated non-game wildlife biologist employed by the United States Fish and Wildlife Service. He is best known as the author of *A Guide to Field Identification/Birds of North America*, now one of the most popular general bird identification guides in use by North American bird watchers. He also is the author of various other works, including *Birds of Maryland and the District of Columbia*. Bird banding, bird distribution, and bird migration are of particular interest to him.

Roberts, Thomas Sadler (1858-1946). A physician and ornithologist best known for his classic *The Birds of Minnesota*.

Robin Dipper. The Bufflehead.

Robin-snipe. A local name for the Red Knot.

Rock-plover. A local name for the Purple Sandpiper.

Rock-snipe. A local name for the Purple Sandpiper.

Rogers, Charles Henry (1888-1977). The respected Curator of Birds at the Princeton University Museum of Zoology and a participant on the first Christmas Bird Count and all subsequent counts except one. He was the teacher of some of America's finest ornithologists.

rookery. A colony of nesting birds such as herons, egrets, or penguins. Also a roosting place for some species of birds.

roost. A location in which large numbers of birds rest or sleep in close proximity to one another. Alternatively, a place where only a single bird rests or sleeps in safety.

Ross, Bernard Rogan (1827-1874). An official of the Hudson Bay Company and a naturalist. Ross' Goose is named in his honor.

Ross, Sir James Clark (1800-1862). A Scottish polar explorer. Ross' Gull is named in his honor.

Rostratulidae. The painted-snipe family.

Rowan, William (1891-1957). A celebrated Canadian ornithologist who discovered and demonstrated that photoperiodism triggered sexual and migration behavior in birds.

Rynchopidae. The family containing the skimmers.

Sabine, Sir Edward (1788-1883). An English explorer, astronomer, and physicist. Sabine's Gull is named in his honor.

sabrewing. Refers to several species of hummingbirds in the genus *Campylopterus*. The Santa Marta Sabrewing is an example.

saltator. Various members of the family Fringillidae. The Grayish Saltator is an example.

sanctuary. An area of land, or water, on which birds and other forms of wildlife are protected and preserved. Hawk Mountain Sanctuary, Pennsylvania, is an example.

sandpiper. Refers to various small shorebirds belonging to the family Scolopacidae. The Least Sandpiper is an example.

sapphire. Refers to certain species of hummingbirds. The Blue-chinned Sapphire is an example.

sapsucker. Refers to several species of woodpeckers. The Yellow-bellied Sapsucker is an example.

Saunders, Aretas Andrews (1884-1970). A noted authority on bird song and author of several books, including *Guide to Bird Song*.

Saunders, William Edwin (1861-1943). A well-known Canadian ornithologist who wrote various articles and books about Canadian birds.

savannah. Open habitat in somewhat arid regions; an area in which a long dry season occurs.

sawbill. Sometimes applied to various merganser species, or to certain species of hummingbirds.

Saw-bill Diver. A local name for the Hooded Merganser.

Say, Thomas (1787-1843). A naturalist and early entomologist who wrote important works about North American insects. Say's Phoebe is named in his honor.

Scape-grace. Another name for the Red-throated Loon.

scapulars. The feathers on a bird's shoulders.

scaup. Refers to several diving ducks, particularly the Greater Scaup and Lesser Scaup.

A Purple Sandpiper. (Photo by Dustin Huntington.)

Schorger, Arlie William (1884-1972). An American chemist and ornithologist best known for his monographs on the Passenger Pigeon and the Wild Turkey. He later served as professor of wildlife ecology at the University of Wisconsin.

Scolopacidae. The sorebird family containing the woodcock, snipe, sandpipers, curlews, and godwits.

scope. A telescope. The term also means to look through a telescope. Thus one scopes a flock of shorebirds or a hawk.

scoter. Refers to several species of sea ducks. The Black Scoter is an example.

Scott, Winfield (1786-1866). The commander of American forces in the Mexican War. Scott's Oriole is named in his honor.

screamer. Refers to the three species in the family Anhimidae. The Horned Screamer is an example.

scythebill. Several species in the family Dendrocolaptidae. The Greater Scythebill is an example.

Sea Duck. A local name for the Common Eider.

sea gull. A layman's term used to refer to gulls without distinction as to species. The Herring Gull is an example of a so-called sea gull.

Sea Robin. Another name for the Red-breasted Merganser.

secondary. A flight feather on the forearm of a bird.

secondary coverts. See **coverts**.

sedentary. A nonmigratory bird.

seedeater. Small finches in the family Fringillidae. The Lined Seedeater is an example.

seed-finch. Various small seed-eating birds of the Neotropics. The Lesser Seed-Finch is an example.

seedsnipe. Refers to four South American species of shorebirds. The White-bellied Seedsnipe is an example.

sexual dimorphism. Refers to differences in appearance between males and females of the same species. Such differences

133

A pair of nesting Blue-eyed Shags in the Antarctic.

may be in size, shape, color, or in other characteristics.

shag. A term used for various species of cormorants, especially several species living in Antarctic and sub-Antarctic areas. The Blue-eyed Shag is an example.

Sharpie. A term used commonly by hawk watchers to refer to a Sharp-shinned Hawk. The term receives frequent use at the many eastern hawk migration lookouts.

shearwater. Refers to various seabirds, such as *Puffinus* and *Procellaria*, in the family Procellariidae. The Sooty Shearwater is an example.

sheathbill. Refers to two South American species in the family Chionididae. The American Sheathbill is an example.

Sheldrake. A local name for the Red-breasted Merganser.

Shellbird. A local name for the Red-breasted Merganser.

Shellduck. A local name for the Red-breasted Merganser.

shorebird. Various species of sandpipers, plovers, curlews, godwits, and related species.

shrike. Refers to species in the family Laniidae. The Northern Shrike is an example.

shrike-tanager. Various tanager species. The Fulvous Shrike-Tanager is an example.

shrike-tyrant. Several species of flycatchers. The Great Shrike-Tyrant is an example.

shrike-vireo. Refers to various tropical species in the family Vireonidae. The Green Shrike-Vireo is an example.

Shufeldt, Robert Wilson (1850-1934). A physician and ornithologist with a particular interest in avian anatomy and osteology. His *Osteology of Birds* is a classic.

Sicklebill. A local name for the Long-billed Curlew.

Sicklebill Curlew. A local name for the Long-billed Curlew.

sierra-finch. Various finches in the family Fringillidae. The Patagonian Sierra-Finch is an example.

Silverback. A local name for the Red Knot.

Silver Plover. Another name for the Red Knot.

Singer, Arthur B. (1917-   ). An internationally known bird and wildlife artist. Most bird watchers instantly recognize Arthur Singer's paintings from their publication in such books as *A Guide to Field Identification/Birds of North America*, *Birds of the World*, *Life of the Hummingbird*, and *Birds of Europe*.

siskin. Various species in the family Fringillidae. The Pine Siskin is an example.

Sittidae. The family containing the nuthatches. The Red-breasted Nuthatch is an example.

skein. A flock of geese in flight.

skimmer. Refers to various species in the family Rynchopidae. The Black Skimmer is an example.

skua. Refers to predatory gull-like birds in the genus *Catharacta*. The Brown Skua is an example.

A nesting Black Skimmer. (Photo by Allan D. Cruickshank.)

Smith, Edmund Stanley "Ned" (1919-   ). A celebrated American wildlife artist whose illustrations appear regularly in leading national and international conservation magazines. His book *Gone for the Day* is a classic, and his illustrations appeared in that book as well as others, including *Complete Book of the Wild Turkey* and *A Field Guide to Birds' Nests*.

Smith, Gideon B. (1793-1867). A British friend of John James Audubon. Smith's Longspur is named in his honor.

Snakebird. Another name for the Anhinga.

snipe. Refers to various species of *Gallinago* and related species. The Giant Snipe is an example.

Snowflake. Another name for the Snow Bunting.

soaring. Flight within a mass of air not uniform in velocity. There are two basic types of soaring: dynamic and static. Seabirds such as albatrosses use dynamic soaring; hawks and other diurnal birds of prey use static soaring.

softtail. Several species in the family Furnariidae. The Orinoco Softtail is an example.

solitaire. Refers to certain species of thrushes. The Andean Solitaire is an example.

song. The voice of a bird, usually used by males in defense of a nest territory.

songbird. Generally refers to the many species of perching birds in the order Passeriformes. Approximately half of the species of birds in the world are considered songbirds of one type or another.

spadebill. Various species of flycatchers. The Russet-winged Spadebill is an example.

sparrow. Refers to various species in the family Fringillidae. The Chipping Sparrow is an example.

species. Groups of interbreeding birds which are reproductively isolated from other groups of birds.

species replacement. A migration term that refers to the staggered peak migration periods used by closely related species, such as the spotted thrushes of North America, so that these species do not arrive in a given area at the same time and compete with each other for available food supplies. Because of staggered peak migration periods, and species replacement, closely related species exhibit a more or less even geographic distribution during the migration seasons.

speculum. A distinctive patch of color on a bird's wing, especially on the wings of certain ducks.

Spheniscidae. The family containing the penguins.

Sphenisciformes. The order containing the penguins.

spinetail. Various members of the family Furnariidae. The Slaty Spinetail is an example.

spoonbill. Several species in the family Threskiornithidae. The Roseate Spoonbill is an example.

Spoonbill Teal. Another name for the Northern Shoveler.

Spotted Brant. Refers to the White-fronted Goose.

Spotted Geese. A colloquial name for the White-fronted Goose.

Sprague, Isaac (1811-1895). A friend of John James Audubon who accompanied him on a trip on the Mississippi River. Sprague's Pipit is named in his honor.

Sprig. Refers to the Common Pintail.

Sprigtail. A local name, sometimes used by hunters, for the Common Pintail.

spring. A flock of teal.

Sprunt, Alexander, Jr. (1898-1973). A noted conversationist, ornithologist, and research biologist for the National Audubon Society. He wrote several books, including *Florida Bird Life.*

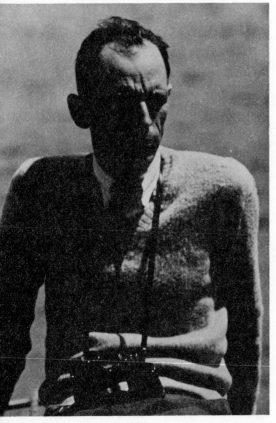

Alexander Sprunt, Jr.
(Photo by Allan D. Cruickshank.)

spur. A horny skin modification, with a bone core, found on the legs of gallinaceous birds and certain other species.

squab. A nestling dove or pigeon.

starfrontlet. Hummingbirds in the genus *Coeligena*. The White-tailed Starfrontlet is an example.

starthroat. Hummingbirds in the genus *Heliomaster*. The Blue-tufted Starthroat is an example.

Steatornithidae. The Oilbird family.

Steller, George Wilhelm (1709-1746). A German Arctic explorer and naturalist. Steller's Eider and Steller's Jay are named in his honor.

steppe. An uncultivated plain without trees.

Stercorariidae. The skua family.

sternum. The breastbone.

stifftail. A general name sometimes applied to diving ducks in the tribe Oxyurini. The Ruddy Duck is an example.

stilt. Refers to some species in the family Recurvirostridae. The Black-necked Stilt is an example.

stint. Several shorebird species in the family Scolopacidae. The Rufous-necked Stint is an example.

Stoddard, Herbert Lee (1889-1968). A celebrated American ornithologist and authority on the Bobwhite.

Stone, Wilmer (1866-1939). A celebrated ornithologist, botanist, and naturalist who served for many years as Curator of Birds at the Academy of Natural Sciences of Philadelphia. He was one of the founders of the Delaware Valley Ornithological Club. His charming *Bird Studies at Old Cape May* is a classic in the literature of American ornithology.

stoop. A very fast, steep descent or dive employed by birds of prey, especially Peregrine Falcons, when attacking prey.

stork. Refers to members of the family Ciconiidae. The Wood Stork is an example.

stratification. See **layering.**

storm petrel. Members of the family Hydrobatidae. The Wilson's Storm Petrel is an example.

Strigidae. The family containing the species of owls except the Barn Owls.

Strigiformes. The order containing all the species of owls.

Strong, Reuben Myron (1872-1964). A celebrated American ornithologist best known for his monumental *A Bibliography of Birds.*

strutting ground. The social display ground or area used by Sage Grouse.

Sturnidae. The family containing the various species of starlings.

The supercilliary, or white eyebrow line, on an adult Northern Goshawk. (Photo by Harry Goldman.)

subspecies. A recognizable and morphologically distinct population within certain species of birds or other animals. Not all species of birds are separated into subspecies. Those birds that are not divided into subspecies are known as monotypic species. Birds with various subspecies are called polytypic species.

sugarbird. Refers to various species of honeycreepers.

Sulidae. The family containing gannets and boobies.

Summer Duck. A local name for the Wood Duck.

summer resident. A species that nests in a particular geographic area, but leaves it and lives in another geographic area during winter.

Summer Teal. A local name for the Blue-winged Teal.

summer visitant. A species that occurs in a given geographic area in summer, but does not nest there.

sunangel. Refers to hummingbirds in the genus *Heliangelus*. The Gorgeted Sunangel is an example.

sunbeam. Refers to hummingbirds in the genus *Aglaeactis*. The Purple-backed Sunbeam is an example.

Sungem. A species of hummingbird.

Sungrebe. Another name for a Finfoot.

supercilliary. A marking, often a line, above the eye of a bird. In some species, such as the Northern Goshawk, the supercilliary is an important field mark which aids bird watchers in making a correct identification of the species.

Sutton, George Miksch (1898-   ). A celebrated American bird artist and ornithologist, considered the dean of American bird artists. He conducted extensive field studies in the Arctic and elsewhere and illustrated many books. Among the many books he wrote are *Birds in the Wilderness, Mexican Birds, Iceland Summer*, and *Oklahoma Birds*. He is Research Professor of Zoology Emeritus at the University of Oklahoma.

Swainson, William (1789-1855). An English naturalist who roamed widely and later became attorney general of New Zealand. Swainson's Hawk, Swainson's Thrush, and Swainson's Warbler honor him.

swallow. Species in the family Hirundinidae. The Cliff Swallow is an example.

A Cliff Swallow at its nest.

Swallowtail. A species of hummingbirds.

Swallow-Tanager. The single species in the family Tersinidae. It lives in tropical South America and on Trinidad.

Swamp Sheldrake. A local name for the Hooded Merganser.

swan. Refers to several species of waterfowl other than geese and ducks. The Whistling Swan is an example.

swift. Members of the family Apodidae. The Chimney Swift is an example.

sylph. Several species of hummingbirds. The Violet-tailed Sylph is an example.

Sylviidae. The Old World warbler family; not to be confused with the wood warblers of the Americas.

syrnix. A bird's voice box.

Whistling Swans in flight.

Taber, Wendell (1897-1960). A well-known New England naturalist who studied the Gray Vireo and contributed species accounts to A. C. Bent's *Life Histories of North American Birds*.

tachuri. Several species of flycatchers. The Bearded Tachuri is an example.

taiga. Coniferous forest located south of North American tundra.

tail. On a bird, the feathers extending behind the rump.

tail coverts. See **coverts**.

talons. The claws of a bird of prey such as a hawk or owl.

tanager. Refers to species in the family Thraupidae. The Scarlet Tanager is an example.

tapaculo. Various species in the family Rhinocryptidae. The White-throated Tapaculo is an example.

tarsus. The ankle.

tattler. Refers to several species of shorebirds in the family Scolopacidae. The Wandering Tattler is an example.

Taverner, Percy Algernon (1875-1947). A well-known Canadian ornithologist who wrote extensively about Canadian birds.

taxonomy. The science of classification of animals and plants. The scientist engaged in such studies is called a taxonomist.

teal. Refers to certain small species of ducks. The Blue-winged Teal is an example.

tern. Birds in the subfamily Sterninae. The Common Tern is an example.

ternery. A colony of nesting terns.

territory. Any geographic area that is defended. There are various kinds of territories, including nesting, hunting, courtship, feeding, and others.

The nest territories of several pairs of American Kestrels on an eastern Pennsylvania farm.
(Reprinted from Heintzelman (1964) in the Wilson Bulletin.

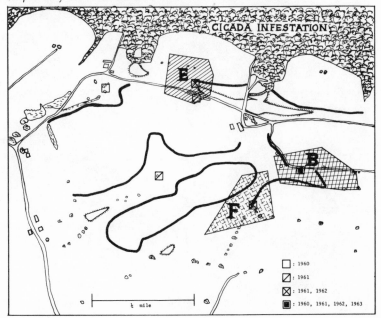

Tersinidae. The swallow-tanager family.

tertials. Wing feathers positioned over the humerus. That is, those wing flight feathers nearest to the body.

Tetraonidae. The grouse family.

Thayer, John Eliot (1862-1933). A well-known ornithologist who collected birds in many areas. Thayer's Gull is named in his honor.

thick-knee. The species in the family Burhinidae. The Peruvian Thick-knee is an example.

Thinocoridae. The seedsnipe family.

Thistletail. Various members of the family Furnariidae. The Puna Thistletail is an example.

thornbill. Various species of hummingbirds. The Black-backed Thornbill is an example.

A Wood Thrush at its nest.

thornbird. Various species in the family Furnariidae. The Greater Thornbird is an example.

thorntail. Hummingbirds in the genus *Popelairia*. The Green Thorntail is an example.

thrasher. Refers to birds in the family Mimidae. The Brown Thrasher is an example.

Thraupidae. The tanager family.

Threskiornithidae. The ibis family.

thrush. Birds in the family Turdidae. The Wood Thrush is an example.

tiercel. A male falcon or hawk.

Timaliidae. The babbler family.

Tinamidae. The family containing the tinamous.

Tinamiformes. The order containing the tinamous.

tinamou. Birds in the family Tinamidae. The Puna Tinamou is an example.

tit. A general name applied to birds in the family Paridae.

titmouse. Various species in the family Paridae. The Tufted Titmouse is an example.

tit-spinetail. Various members of the family Furnariidae. The Andean Tit-Spinetail is an example.

tit-tyrant. Several flycatcher species. The Tufted Tit-Tyrant is an example.

tityra. Cotingas in the genus *Tityra*. The Masked Tityra is an example.

toboganning. A method of locomotion used by penguins whereby they slide along on their bellies on snow.

Todd, Walter Edmund Clyde (1874-1969). A venerable ornithologist from the Carnegie Museum of Natural History and author of such classics as *Birds of Western Pennsylvania* and *Birds of the Labrador Peninsula*.

Todidae. The tody family.

tody. Refers to birds in the family Todidae. Todies are endemic to the West Indies.

tody-flycatcher. Various small species of flycatchers. The Ruddy Tody-Flycatcher is an example.

tody-tyrant. Various small flycatchers. The Yungas Tody-Tyrant is an example.

topaz. Various species of hummingbirds in the genus *Topaza*. The Fiery Topaz is an example.

topography. See **bird topography**.

toucan. Various birds in the family Ramphastidae. The Keel-billed Toucan is an example.

toucanet. Refers to various small toucans in the family Ramphastidae. The Yellow-billed Toucanet is an example.

towhee. Refers to several species in the genera *Pipilo* and *Chlarura*. The Rufous-sided Towhee is an example.

Townsend, John Kirk (1809-1851). A widely traveled naturalist, ornithologist, and friend of John James Audubon. Townsend's Solitaire and Townsend's Warbler are named in his honor.

trachea. The windpipe.

Traill, Thomas Stewart (1781-1862). A friend of John James Audubon and respected British citizen. Traill's Flycatcher is named in his honor.

train. A falconer's term for a hawk's tail.

trainbrearer. Refers to several species of hummingbirds or trogons.

tree-duck. An obsolete term used for various species of whistling ducks.

treehunter. Various species in the family Furnariidae. The Flammulated Treehunter is an example.

treerunner. Several species in the family Furnariidae. The Pearled Treerunner is an example.

Trochilidae. The hummingbird family.

Troglodytidae. The wren family.

trogon. Various birds in the family Trogonidae. The Masked Trogan is an example.

Trogonidae. The family containing the trogons.

Trogoniformes. The order containing the trogons.

Troop-fowl. The Greater Scaup.

tropicbird. Species in the family Phaethontidae. The Red-tailed Tropicbird is an example.

A Red-tailed Tropicbird. (Photo by David B. Marshall/U.S. Fish and Wildlife Service.)

Trudeau, James deBertz (1817-1887). A friend of John James Audubon. Trudeau's Tern is named in his honor.

trumpeter. Species in the family Psophiidae. The Gray-winged Trumpeter is an example. The term also is used occasionally to refer to the Trumpeter Swan.

tubenoses. A general name applied to pelagic birds in the order Procellariiformes. Among the species included under the term are albatrosses, petrels, shearwaters, storm petrels, and diving-petrels.

tuftedcheek. Several Furnariidae species. The Buffy Tuftedcheek is an example.

Turdidae. The thrush family.

Turnbull, William P. (1830-1871). A relatively obscure ornithologist and author of *The Birds of East Pennsylvania and New Jersey*.

tundra. Arctic habitat consisting of frozen or partly frozen mosses, lichens, and swamplike vegetation.

turaco. Species in the family Musophagidae.

turnstone. Several shorebird species in the family Scolopacidae. The Ruddy Turnstone is an example.

A Black Turnstone. (Photo by Dustin Huntington.)

Tyrannidae. The species of New World or tyrant flycatchers.

tyrannulet. Various species of flycatchers. The Yellow Tyrannulet is an example.

tyrant. Several species of flycatchers, for example the Longtailed Tyrant.

tyrant-manakin. Several species in the family Pipridae. The Pale-bellied Tyrant-Manakin is an example.

Tytonidae. The family containing the Barn Owl.

umbrellabird. Two species in the family Cotingidae. The Amazonian Umbrellabird is an example.

undertail coverts. See **coverts**.

uppertail coverts. See **coverts**.

Urner Club. Refers to the Urner Ornithological Club of Newark, New Jersey. The organization is an old and particularly well-respected bird-study society.

Urner Field Observer. The journal published by the Urner Ornithological Club of Newark, New Jersey.

vagrant. A bird that has strayed outside of the normal geographic range for the species or subspecies. Bird watchers
eagerly look for vagrants.

vagrant migration. Notable invasions of birds outside of their
normal geographic range. Crossbills, for example, sometimes engage in vagrant migrations. See also **invasion**.

vane. The webs of a feather, consisting of the barbs attached
to the rachis or shaft.

Van Tyne, Josselyn (1902-1956). A well-known and important
ornithologist who was Curator of Birds at the Museum of
Zoology at the University of Michigan. His textbook *Fundamentals of Ornithology*, written with Andrew J. Berger, is a
standard ornithological reference.

Vaurie, Charles (1906-1975). A noted ornithologist from the
American Museum of Natural History who wrote extensively about birds; his two-volume *Birds of the Palearctic Fauna*
is particularly well known.

A Turkey Vulture in flight.

Vaux, William S. (1811-1882). A member of the Academy of National Sciences of Philadelphia. Vaux's Swift is named for him.

Veery. A species of thrush.

vegetation. The plantlife of an area.

vent. A bird's cloacal opening. The anus.

ventral. Relating to the abdomen. Refers to the lower surface of a bird or other animal; the underside.

vermiculations. Fine wavy lines. Vermiculations occur in the plumage of certain birds including some species of waterfowl.

vernacular name. The common name of a bird. An example is Wood Thrush.

vertebrate. An animal with a backbone. All birds are vertebrates.

vertical migration. The seasonal movement of some species of birds to higher or lower elevations on the side of a mountain. Williamson's Sapsuckers, for example, engage in vertical migrations in the Rocky Mountains.

violetear. Hummingbirds in the genus *Colibri*. The Green Violetear is an example.

vireo. Birds in the subfamily Vireoninae (family Vireonidae). The Red-eyed Vireo is an example.

Vireonidae. The family containing vireos, greenlets, shrike-vireos, and peppershrikes.

visitor. A bird that occurs in a geographic area at certain periods of the year but not year-round.

visorbearer. Several tropical species of hummingbirds. The Hooded Visorbearer is an example.

vulture. A carrion-eating bird of prey belonging to the family Cathartidae. The Turkey Vulture is an example.

wader. Shorebird. The term is used more commonly in Britain and Europe than in North America.

wagtail. Various species in the family Motacillidae. The Gray Wagtail is an example.

wagtail-tyrant. Several species of small flycatchers. The Greater Wagtail-Tyrant is an example.

warbler. Refers to wood warblers in the family Parulidae. The Black-throated Green Warbler is an example.

warbling-finch. Various members of the family Fringillidae. The Collared Warbling-Finch is an example.

waterfowl. Refers to swans, geese, and ducks in the family Anatidae.

waterfowler. A sportsman who hunts waterfowl.

waterthrush. Refers to two species of wood warblers in the genus *Seiurus*. The Northern Waterthrush is an example.

water-tyrant. Several species of flycatchers. The Pied Water-Tyrant is an example.

An adult Black-throated Green Warbler (right) feeding a young Brown-headed Cowbird.

A Cedar Waxwing.
(Photo by Dustin Huntington.)

waxwing. Refers to birds in the family Bombycillidae. The Cedar Waxwing is an example.

Wayne, Arthur Trezevant (1863-1930). An American ornithologist best known for his *Birds of South Carolina*.

weaver. Refers to the many species in the family Ploceidae. The House Sparrow is an example.

weaver-finch. See **weaver**.

web. The vane of a feather; also, a membrane betwen two toes on a bird's foot.

Wetmore, Alexander (1886-1978). A celebrated American ornithologist and originator of the Wetmore sequence of bird classification. He was a former secretary of the Smithsonian Institution, an expert on fossil birds, and an author of numerous scientific papers about birds. His multi-volume *The Birds of Panama* is a classic.

whalebird. A name used by sailors for various species of petrels.

Whistler. A local name for the Common Goldeneye.

Whitefront. Another name for the White-fronted Goose.

whistling duck. Refers to various abberant species of ducks in the genus *Dendrocygna*. The Black-bellied Whistling Duck is an example.

A Black-bellied Whistling Duck.

A pair of American Widgeons.

White-belly. An obscure name for the American Wigeon.

Whooper. Another name for the Whooper Swan.

widgeon. An alternative spelling of "wigeon."

Wied, Prince Maximilian zu (1782-1867). A German naturalist. Wied's Crested Flycatcher is named for him.

wigeon. Refers to several species of ducks in the genus *Anas*. The American Wigeon is an example.

wildfowl. Refers to swans, geese, and ducks in the family Anatidae.

Williamson, Robert Stockton (1824-1881). An officer in the United States Army who was charged with the operation of the Pacific Railroad Survey to northern California and Oregon. Williamson's Sapsucker is named in his honor.

Wilson, Alexander (1766-1813). The father of American ornithology.

wing. A bird's forelimb.

wing coverts. See **coverts**.

wing lining. The coverts lining the ventral or lower surface of a bird's wing.

winter finch. Used by bird watchers to refer to northern finches, grosbeaks, crossbills, and related species which sometimes are seen during winter in an area but which do not occur there at other seasons of the year—particularly during the breeding season.

wintering grounds. The geographic area in which the members of a species spend the winter.

Winter Snipe. A local name for the Purple Sandpiper.

Winter Teal. A local name for the Green-winged Teal.

winter visitant. A species that spends the winter in one geographic area, but migrates to another area to nest.

wisp. A flock of snipe.

woodcreeper. Refers to birds in the family Dencrocolaptidae. The Long-billed Woodcreeper is an example.

Wood Duck. A vividly colored (male only) species of waterfowl and a popular game bird.

woodhewer. See **woodcreeper**.

woodnymph. Refers to several species of hummingbirds in the genus *Thalurania*. The Fork-tailed Woodnymph is an example.

A male Wood Duck.

A Red-bellied Woodpecker.
(Photo by Harry Goldman.)

woodpecker. Refers to various birds in the family Picidae. The Downy Woodpecker and Red-bellied Woodpecker are examples.

wood-quail. Refers to various species in the family Phasianidae. The Chestnut Wood-Quail is an example.

wood-rail. Various species in the family Rallidae. The Gray-necked Wood-Rail is an example.

Wood Sheldrake. A local name for the Hooded Merganser.

woodstar. Refers to certain species of hummingbirds. The Purple-collared Woodstar is an example.

wood warbler. See **warbler**.

wood-wren. Several species of tropical wrens. The Gray-breasted Wood-Wren is an example.

wren. The species of birds in the family Troglodytidae. The House Wren is an example.

Xantus de Vescy, Louis Jonas (1825-1894). A Hungarian naturalist who collected birds in the western United States. Xantus' Murrelet is named for him.

xenops. Several species in the family Furnariidae. The Great Xenops is an example.

yellow-finch. Various small finches. The Puna Yellow-Finch is an example.

yellowlegs. Refers to two species of shorebirds—the Greater Yellowlegs and the Lesser Yellowlegs.

young. Nestling birds.

Zeledoniidae. The wren-thrush family.

zoology. The science concerned with the study of animals.

Zugunruhe. A German term meaning pre-migratory restlessness in birds.

APPENDIX

NATIONAL BIRD WATCHING
AND ORNITHOLOGICAL ORGANIZATIONS

American Birding Association
P.O. Box 4335
Austin, Texas 78765

American Ornithologists' Union
c/o Smithsonian Institution
Washington, D.C. 20560

Bird Populations Institute
Kansas State University
P.O. Box 637
Manhattan, Kansas 66502

Cornell Laboratory of Ornithology
159 Sapsucker Woods Road
Ithaca, New York 14850

National Audubon Society
950 Third Avenue
New York, New York 10022

National Wildlife Federation
1412 Sixteenth St., N.W.
Washington, D.C. 20036

Wilson Ornithological Society
c/o Division of Birds
Museum of Zoology
University of Michigan
Ann Arbor, Michigan 48104